# Introduction to Data Mining and SAS® Enterprise Miner™

Course Notes

*Introduction to Data Mining and SAS® Enterprise Miner™ Course Notes* was developed by Tom Bohannon. Additional contributions were made by André de Waal. Editing and production support was provided by the Curriculum Development and Support Department.



**Introduction to Data Mining and SAS® Enterprise Miner™ Course Notes**



Book code E2101, course code EMIW71, prepared date 29Sep2011. EMIW71_001

ISBN 978-1-61290-128-2

# Table of Contents

## To learn more…

For information about other courses in the curriculum, contact the SAS Education Division at 1-800-333-7660, or send e-mail to training@sas.com. You can also find this information on the Web at support.sas.com/training/ as well as in the Training Course Catalog.

For a list of other SAS books that relate to the topics covered in this Course Notes, USA customers can contact our SAS Publishing Department at 1-800-727-3228 or send e-mail to sasbook@sas.com. Customers outside the USA, please contact your local SAS office.

Also, see the Publications Catalog on the Web at support.sas.com/pubs for a complete list of books and a convenient order form.

# Chapter 1 Predictive Modeling With SAS® Enterprise Miner™

# 1.1 Introduction to Enterprise Miner

## Objectives

- Discuss some of the history of data mining.
- Define data mining.
- Identify some of the issues surrounding data mining.
- Highlight some applications of data mining.

3

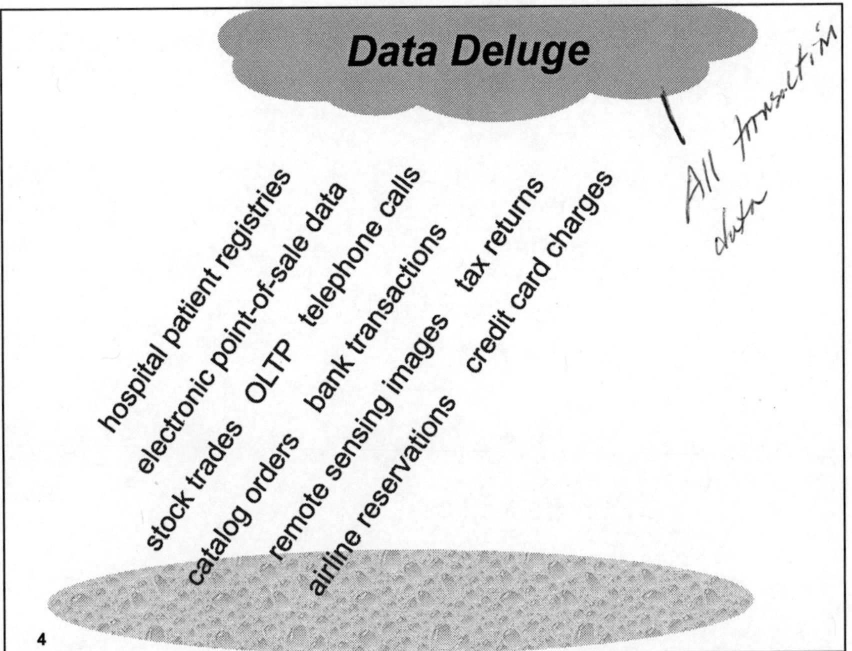


The data deluge is the result of the prevalence of automatic data collection, electronic instrumentation, and online transactional processing (OLTP). There is a growing recognition of the untapped value in these databases. This recognition is driving the development of data mining and data warehousing.

## The Data

| | Experimental | Opportunistic |
|---|---|---|
| **Purpose** | Research | Operational |
| **Value** | Scientific | Commercial |
| **Generation** | Actively controlled | Passively observed |
| **Size** | Small | Massive |
| **Hygiene** | Clean | Dirty |
| **State** | Static | Dynamic |

5

Historically, most data was generated or collected for research purposes. Today, businesses have massive amounts of operational data. This operational data was not generated with data analysis in mind. It is aptly characterized as *opportunistic* (Huber 1997). This is in contrast to experimental data where factors are controlled and varied in order to answer specific questions.

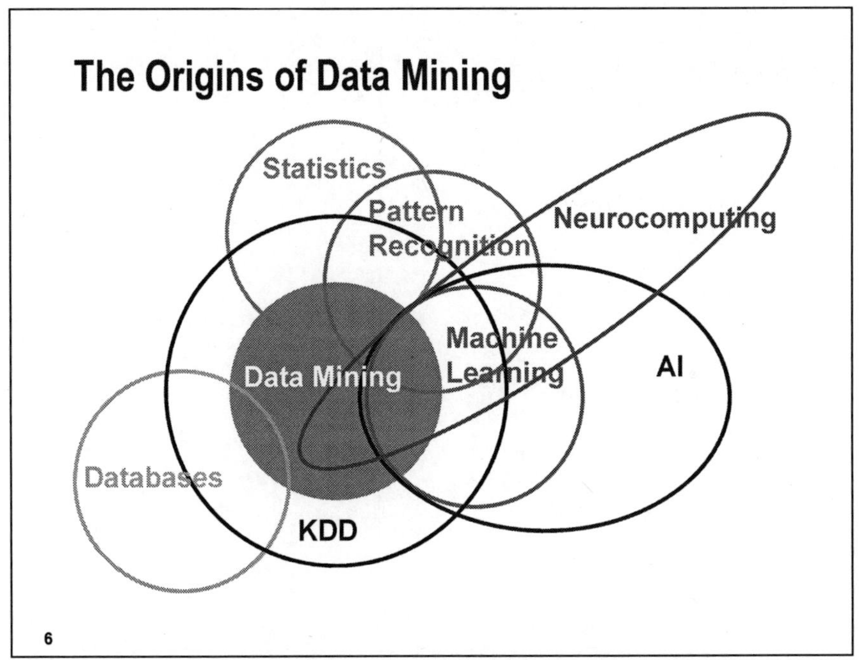


The analytical tools used in data mining were developed mainly by statisticians, artificial intelligence (AI) researchers, and database system researchers.

KDD (knowledge discovery in databases) was formed in 1989 as a multidisciplinary research area concerned with the extraction of patterns from large databases. KDD is often used synonymously with data mining. More precisely, data mining is considered a single step in the overall discovery process.

Machine learning is a branch of AI concerned with creating and understanding semiautomatic learning methods.

Pattern recognition has its roots in engineering and is typically concerned with image classification. Pattern recognition methodology crosses over many areas.

Neurocomputing is a multidisciplinary field concerned with neural networks.

## Solving the Data Puzzle: A Step-by-Step Approach

1. Business question
2. Data collection
3. Data organization
4. Data analysis
5. Reporting
6. Action

7

The first step in the process must be the definition of a business question or problem. If there is no question to be answered or problem to be solved, then the rest of the process is not necessary.

When the problem or question has been identified, then you can determine the data that you believe will be necessary to answer that question or begin to solve the problem. This data might already be collected in transactional systems or in existing customer information systems. In some cases, however, you identify new data that needs to be collected.

The mere existence of data does not mean that you can analyze it. You must first organize the data for analysis. In some cases, this could mean combining various databases into a single data source. In other cases, this could be reorganizing the data tables for analysis. This step can be as complex as building a data warehouse or data mart or as simple as joining data tables depending upon your environment.

As the next step in the process, you can begin to analyze the data. This is the part of the process that SAS Enterprise Miner handles. In SAS Enterprise Miner, the analysis itself is broken up into steps: sample, explore, modify, model, and assess (SEMMA). This approach and the corresponding steps are discussed in the next section of this course.

The data analysis results then need to be summarized into a report to be delivered to management. This should result in some sort of action taken such as the following:

- a decision to adopt a model for use in determining the credit worthiness of loan applicants
- a mechanism to determine which customers to contact about a new product
- a way to identify potentially fraudulent healthcare claims
- the recognition of the need to collect additional data to answer the question at hand

In general, some sort of business decision flows out of this process.

## What Is Data Mining?

- Complicated database queries
  - Obtaining information about customers or groups of customers from a data warehouse for marketing or other purposes
  - The process of sorting through large amounts of data and picking out relevant information
- What you are taught not to do in traditional statistics classes
  - Data mining is derogatory. It means sorting through a huge volume of data and extracting decision rules without regard to the underlying assumptions of the methods used.

8

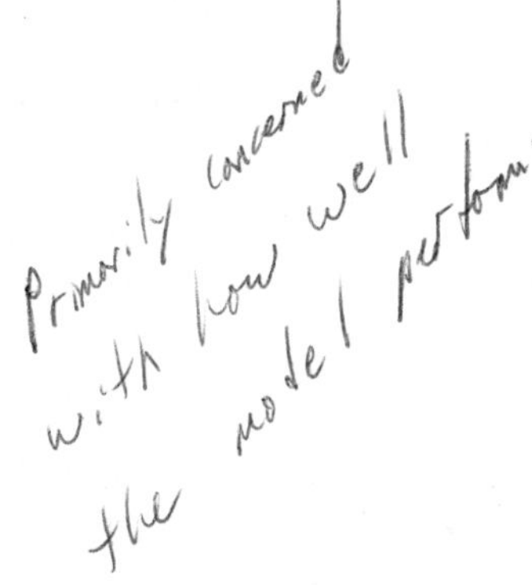

Primarily concerned
with how well
the model performs


Because of the varied origins of the tools used, there are a multitude of definitions of data mining. Depending on the background of a given individual or group, you are likely to get very different definitions of the term.

The database community has a tendency to view data mining methods as more complicated types of database queries. For example, standard query tools can answer questions such as "How many surgeries resulted in hospital stays longer than 10 days?" But data mining is needed for more complicated queries, such as "What are the important preoperative predictors of excessive length of stay?" This view has led many to confuse data mining with query tools. For example, many consider OLAP (online analytical processing), which is software for interactive access, query, and summarization of multidimensional data warehouses, to be data mining. To some, the objective of data mining is merely to implement query tools. In this case, there is no specific problem to formulate, and sophisticated analytical methods are not relevant.

## Data Mining: The SAS Definition

Data mining is an iterative process of creating predictive and descriptive models, by uncovering previously unknown trends and patterns in vast amounts of data, in order to support decision making.

9

## Required Expertise

- Domain
- Data
- Analytical Methods

10

- The *domain expert* understands the particulars of the business or scientific problem: the relevant background knowledge, context, and terminology; and the strengths and deficiencies of the current solution (if a current solution exists).
- The *data expert* understands the structure, size, and format of the data.
- The *analytical expert* understands the capabilities and limitations of the methods that might be relevant to the problem.

The embodiment of this expertise might take up to three or more people.

## Skepticism and Communication

- Skepticism
  - Breaking the rules
  - Magic
- Communication

11

After the data has been analyzed (and conclusions drawn by the analysts), the results are often met with mixed reactions. There is a lot of skepticism about data mining results. Traditional statisticians see data mining as "breaking the rules." The assumptions for some of the statistical algorithms used are often ignored, leading the traditional statistician to conclude that the models are invalid and worthless. On the other end of the spectrum, non-analytic individuals might see data mining as a magical black box. No one can explain what happens inside the software; they just input the data and come out with a model. If it is that magical, it cannot be good to make business decisions based on the results.

Along those lines, it is important for the data mining experts to make the effort to explain the potentially complex models to the non-analytic individuals who might be responsible for making those business decisions. The explanation needs to demystify the process and make business sense to the listener.

## Some Application Areas

**Market Basket Analysis**

- Banks – to detect which customers are using which products so they can offer the right mix of products and services to better meet customer needs: cross-sell and up-sell
- Retail – to determine what products customers tend to purchase together to assist in developing marketing strategies

12

## Some Application Areas

**Predictive Modeling**

- Credit card companies – to assist in mailing promotional materials to people who are most likely to respond
- Lenders – to determine which applicants are most likely to default on a loan
- Universities – to predict which students will remain enrolled after the first year and/or through graduation
- Nonprofit organizations – to determine who is most likely to donate and how much they might donate

13

## Objectives

- Explore the workspace components of SAS Enterprise Miner.
- Define SEMMA.
- Introduce the tools available in SAS Enterprise Miner.

14

## SAS Enterprise Miner

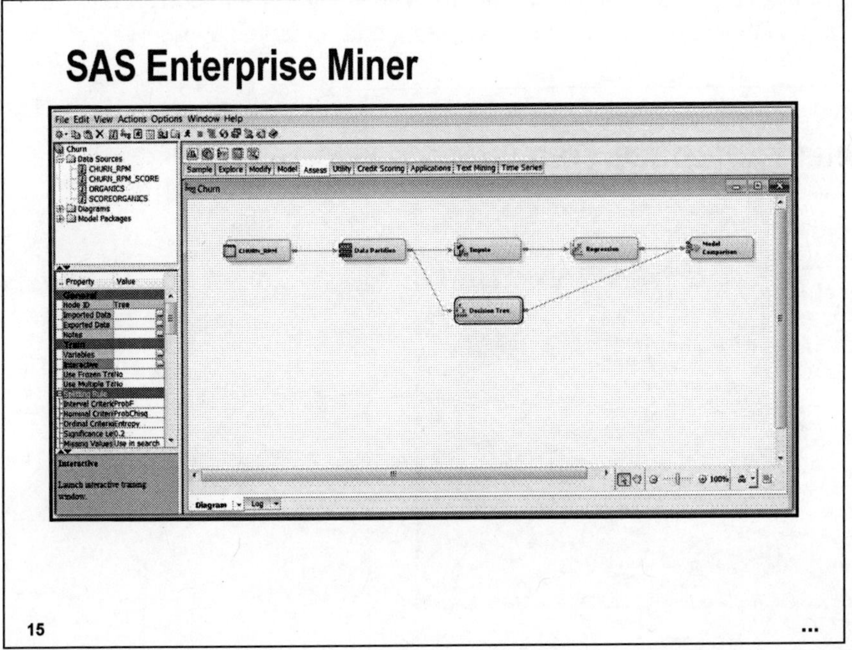


15 ...

The SAS Enterprise Miner 7.1 interface simplifies many common tasks associated with applied analysis. It offers secure analysis management and provides a wide variety of tools with a consistent graphical interface. You can even customize it by incorporating your own analysis methods and tools.

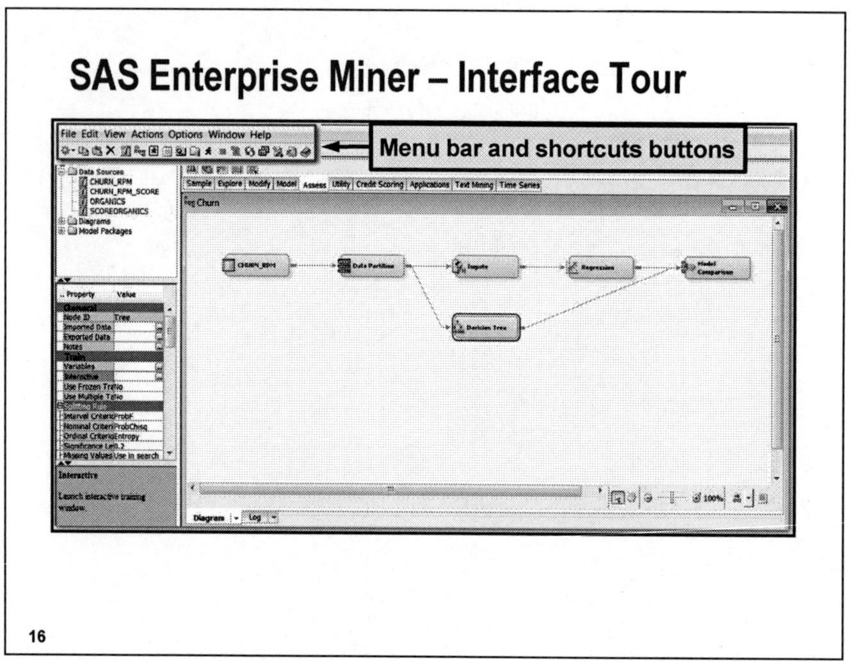


The interface window is divided into several functional components. The *menu bar* and corresponding *shortcut buttons* perform the usual windows tasks, as well as start, stop, and review analyses.

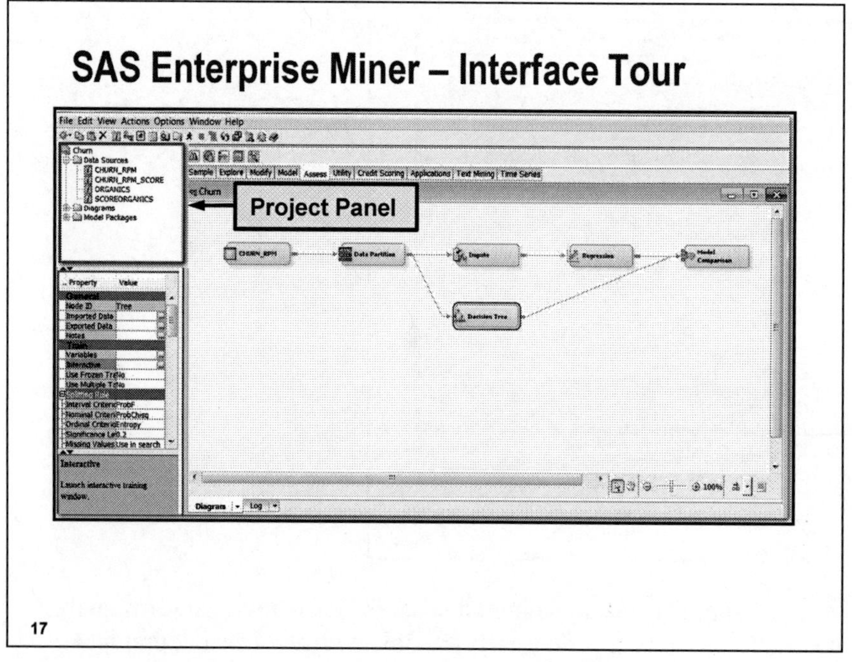


The *Project panel* manages and views data sources, diagrams, results, and project users. You may have only one project open at a time. Projects are automatically saved when they are closed.

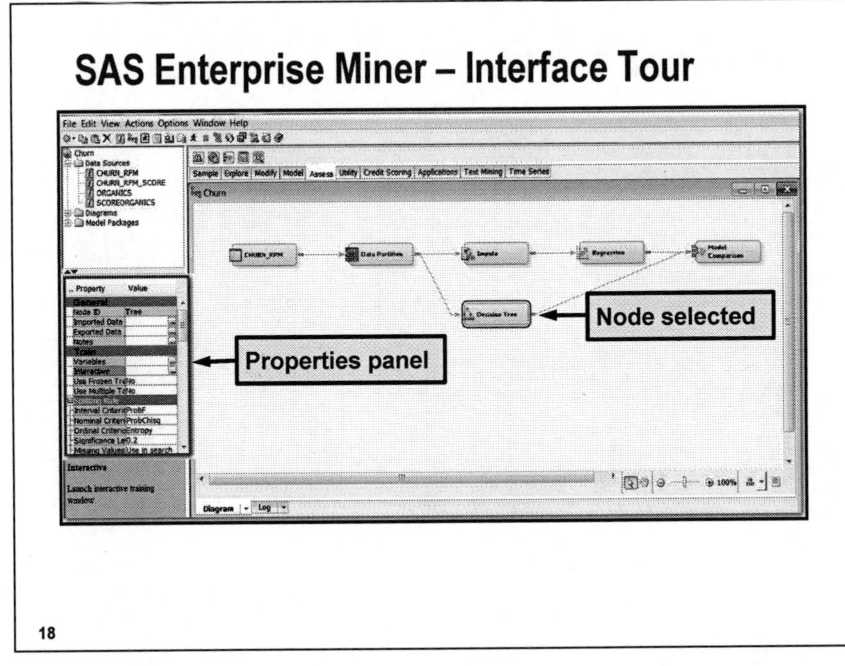


Node is and app to do a specific task
manipulate properties to modify the node

The *Properties panel* enables you to view and edit the settings of data sources, diagrams, nodes, results, and users. When a node is selected in the diagram the property panel for that node appears.

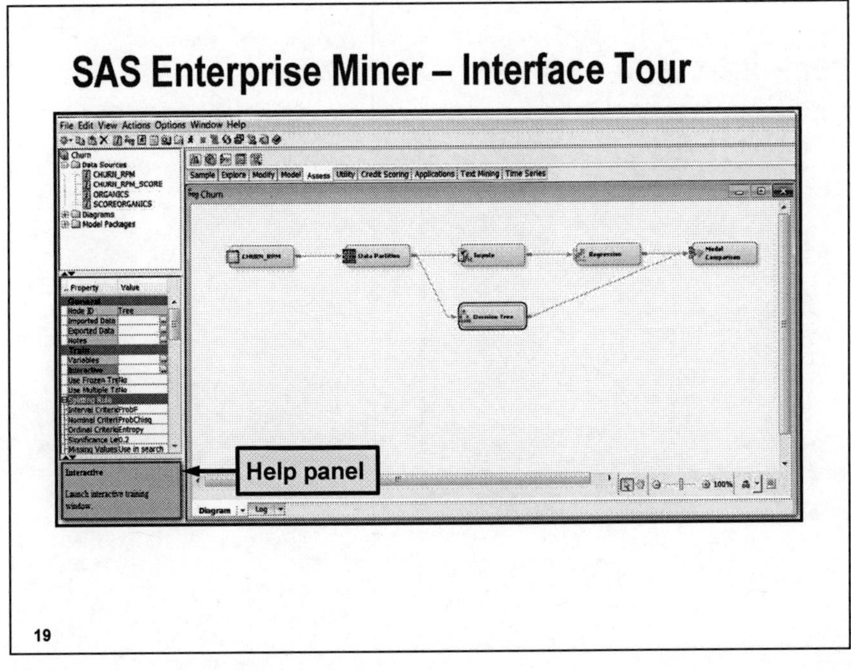


Context sensitive

The *Help panel* displays a short description of the property that you select in the Properties panel. Extended help can be found in the Help Topics selection from the Help main menu.

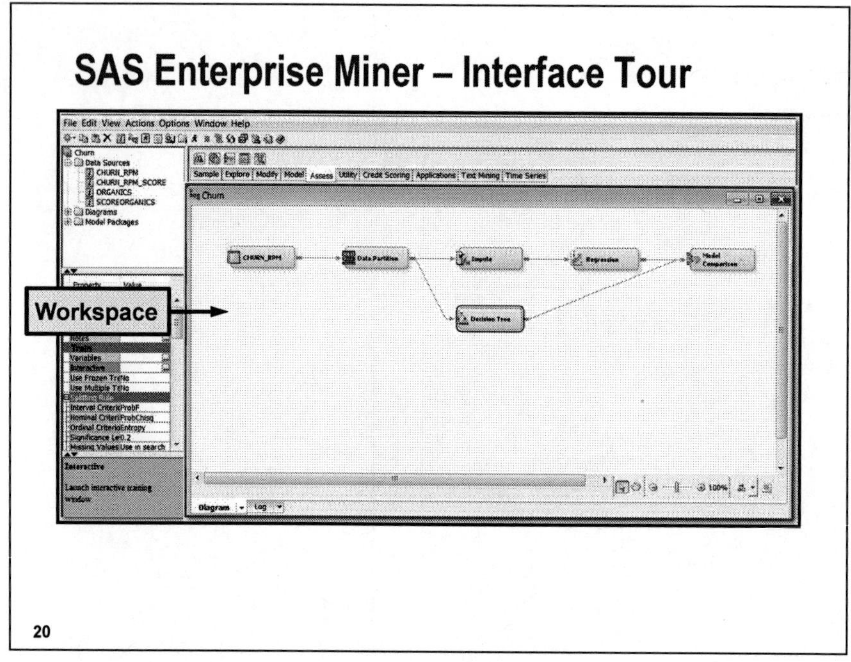

In the *diagram workspace*, process flow diagrams are built, edited, and run. The workspace is where you graphically sequence the tools that you use to analyze your data and generate reports.

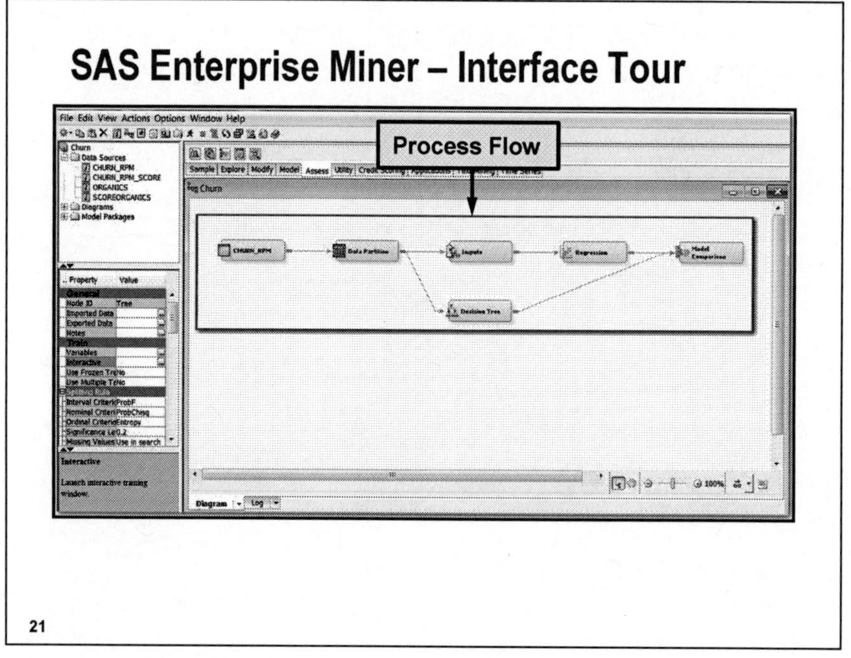


The diagram workspace contains one or more *process flows*. A process flow starts with a data source and sequentially applies SAS Enterprise Miner tools to complete your analytic objective.

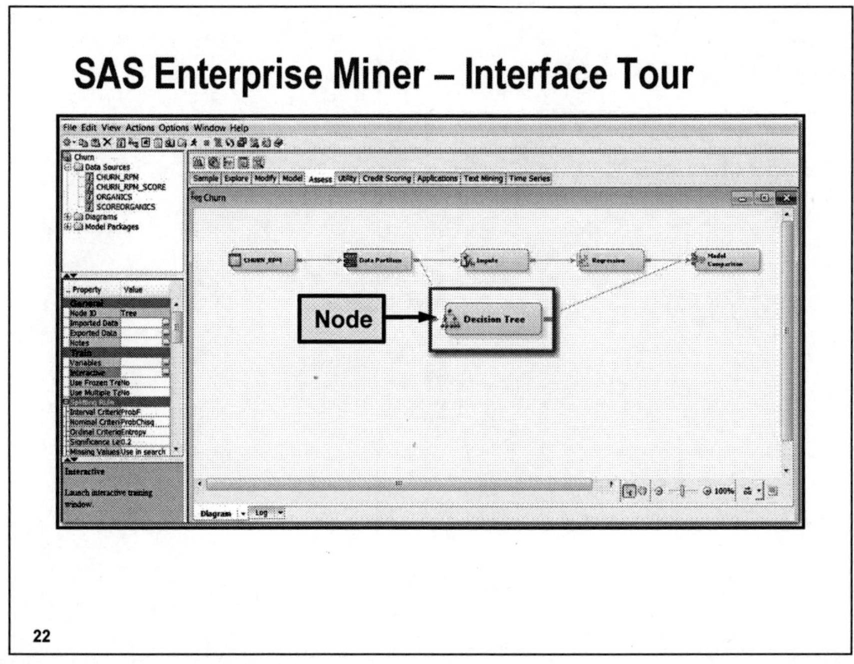


A process flow contains several *nodes*. Nodes are SAS Enterprise Miner tools connected by arrows to show the direction of information flow in an analysis.

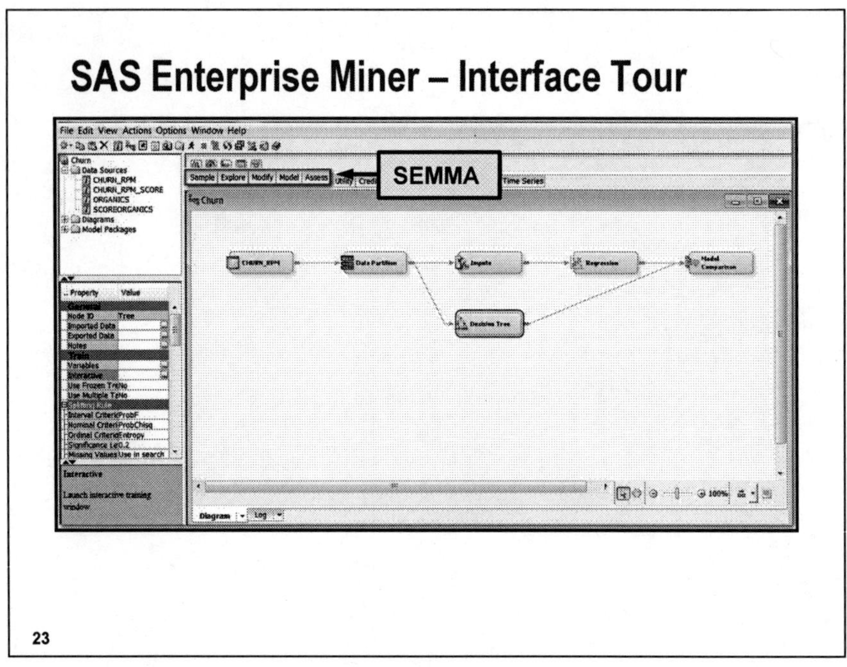


The SAS Enterprise Miner tools available to your analysis are contained in the *tools palette*. The tools palette is arranged according to the SAS process for data mining, SEMMA.

SEMMA stands for

**S**ample – You sample the data by creating one or more data tables. The samples should be large enough to contain the significant information, yet small enough to process.

**E**xplore – You explore the data by searching for anticipated relationships, unanticipated trends, and anomalies in order to gain understanding and ideas.

**M**odify – You modify the data by creating, selecting, and transforming the variables to focus the model selection process.

**M**odel – You model the data by using the analytical tools to search for a combination of the data that reliably predicts a desired outcome.

**A**ssess – You assess competing predictive models (build charts to evaluate the usefulness and reliability of the findings from the data mining process).

Additional tools are available under the Utility group and, if licensed, the Credit Scoring and Text Mining groups.

## SEMMA – Sample Tab

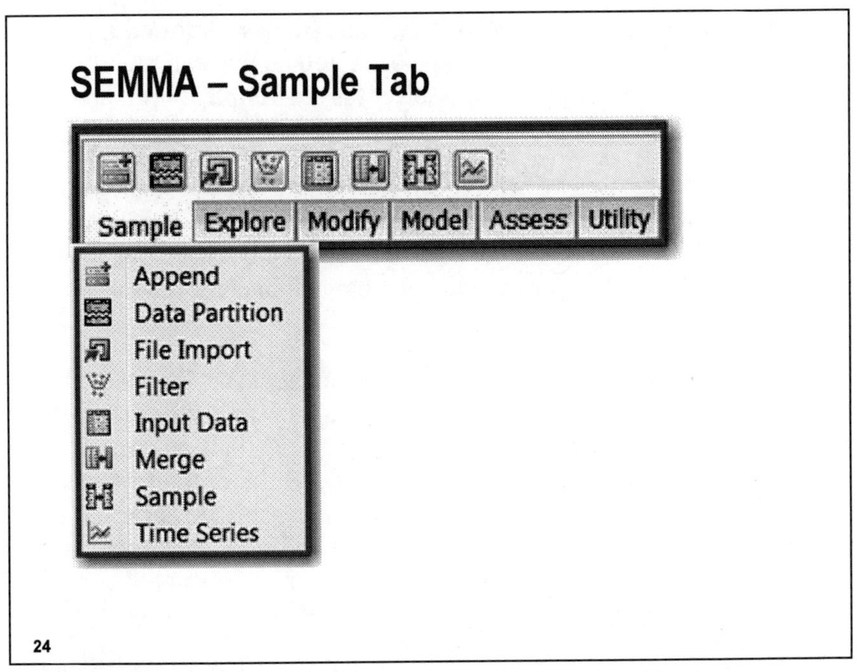


24

Each tab has a variety of tools.

The **Append** tool is used to append data sets that are exported by two different paths in a single process flow diagram. The Append tool can also append train, validation, and test data sets into a new training data set.

The **Input Data** tool represents the data source that you choose for your mining analysis and provides details (metadata) about the variables in the data source that you want to use.

The **File Import** tool enables you to convert selected external flat files, spreadsheets, and database tables into a format that Enterprise Miner recognizes as a data source and can use in data mining process flow diagrams.

The **Filter** tool creates and applies filters to your training data set and, optionally, to the validation and test data sets. You can use filters to exclude certain observations, such as extreme outliers and errant data, that you do not want to include in your mining analysis.

The **Merge** tool enables you to merge observations from two or more data sets into a single observation in a new data set. The Merge tool supports both one-to-one and matches merging.

The **Data Partition** tool enables you to partition data sets into training, test, and validation data sets. The training data set is used for preliminary model fitting. The validation data set is used to monitor and tune the model during estimation and is also used for model assessment. The test data set is an additional holdout data set that you can use for model assessment. This tool uses simple random sampling, stratified random sampling, or cluster sampling to create partitioned data sets.

The **Sample** tool enables you to take simple random samples, $n^{th}$ observation samples, stratified random samples, first-*n* samples, and cluster samples of data sets. For any type of sampling, you can specify either a number of observations or a percentage of the population to select for the sample. If you are working with rare events, the Sample tool can be configured for oversampling or stratified sampling.

Sampling is recommended for extremely large databases because it can significantly decrease model training time. If the sample is sufficiently representative, relationships found in the sample can be expected to generalize to the complete data set. The Sample tool writes the sampled observations to an output data set and saves the seed values that are used to generate the random numbers for the samples so that you can replicate the samples.

The **Time Series** tool converts transactional data to time series data. Transactional data is time-stamped data that is collected over time at no particular frequency. By contrast, time series data is time-stamped data that is summarized over time at a specific frequency. You might have many suppliers and many customers, as well as transaction data that is associated with both. The size of each set of transactions can be very large, which makes many traditional data mining tasks difficult. By condensing the information into a time series, you can discover trends and seasonal variations in customer and supplier habits that might not be visible in transactional data.

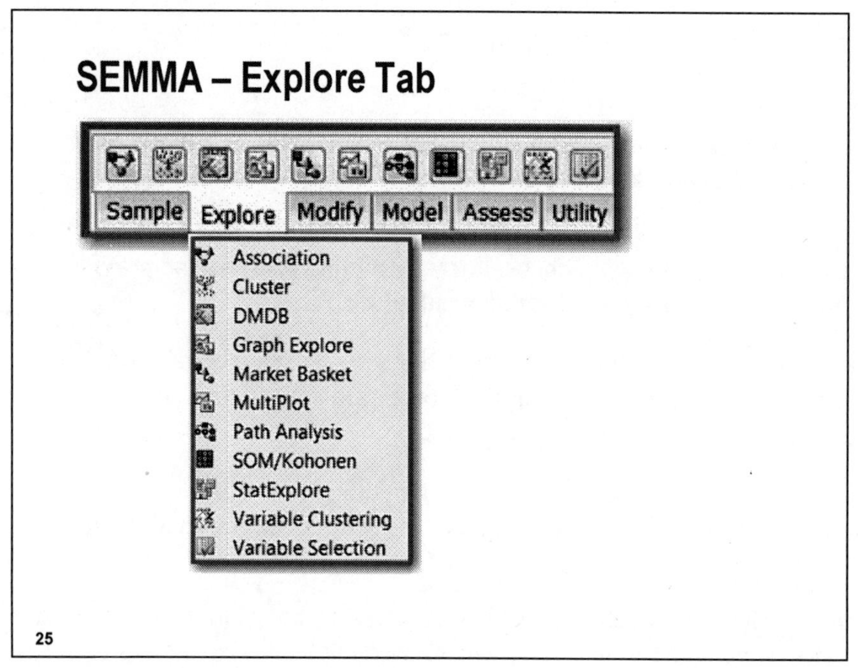

The **Association** tool enables you to perform association discovery to identify items that tend to occur together within the data. For example, if a customer buys a loaf of bread, how likely is the customer to also buy a gallon of milk? This type of discovery is also known as *market basket analysis*. The tool also enables you to perform sequence discovery if a timestamp variable (a sequence variable) is present in the data set. This enables you to take into account the ordering of the relationships among items.

The **Cluster** tool enables you to segment your data; that is, it enables you to identify data observations that are similar in some way. Observations that are similar tend to be in the same cluster, and observations that are different tend to be in different clusters. The cluster identifier for each observation can be passed to subsequent tools in the diagram.

The **DMDB** tool creates a data mining database that provides summary statistics and factor-level information for class and interval variables in the imported data set.

The **Graph Explore** tool is an advanced visualization tool that enables you to explore large volumes of data graphically to uncover patterns and trends and to reveal extreme values in the database. The tool creates a run-time sample of the input data source. You use the Graph Explore node to interactively explore and analyze your data using graphs. Your exploratory graphs are remembered when the Graph Explore Results window is closed. When you reopen the Graph Explore Results window, the graphs are re-created.

The experimental **Market Basket** tool performs association rule mining over transaction data in conjunction with item taxonomy. Transaction data contains sales transaction records with details about items bought by customers. Market basket analysis uses the information from the transaction data to give us insight about which products tend to be purchased together.

The **MultiPlot** tool is a visualization tool that enables you to explore large volumes of data graphically. The MultiPlot tool automatically creates bar charts and scatter plots for the input and target. The code created by this tool can be used to create graphs in a batch environment.

The **Path Analysis** tool enables you to analyze Web log data to determine the paths that visitors take as they navigate through a Web site. You can also use the tool to perform sequence analysis.

The **SOM/Kohonen** tool performs unsupervised learning by using Kohonen vector quantization (VQ), Kohonen self-organizing maps (SOMs), or batch SOMs with Nadaraya-Watson or local-linear smoothing. Kohonen VQ is a clustering method, whereas SOMs are primarily dimension-reduction methods. For cluster analysis, the Clustering tool is recommended instead of Kohonen VQ or SOMs.

The **StatExplore** tool is a multipurpose tool used to examine variable distributions and statistics in your data sets. The tool generates summarization statistics. You can use the StatExplore tool to do the following:

- select variables for analysis, for profiling clusters, and for predictive models
- compute standard univariate distribution statistics
- compute standard bivariate statistics by class target and class segment
- compute correlation statistics for interval variables by interval input and target

The **Variable Clustering** tool is useful for data reduction, such as choosing the best variables or cluster components for analysis. Variable clustering removes collinearity, decreases variable redundancy, and helps to reveal the underlying structure of the input variables in a data set.

The **Variable Selection** tool enables you to evaluate the importance of input variables in predicting or classifying the target variable. To select the important inputs, the tool uses either an R-squared or a Chi-squared selection criterion. The R-squared criterion enables you to remove variables in hierarchies, remove variables that have large percentages of missing values, and remove class variables that are based on the number of unique values. The variables that are not related to the target are set to a status of **Rejected**. Although rejected variables are passed to subsequent tools in the process flow diagram, these variables are not used as model inputs by more detailed modeling tools, such as the Neural Network and Decision Tree tools. You can reassign the input model status to rejected variables.

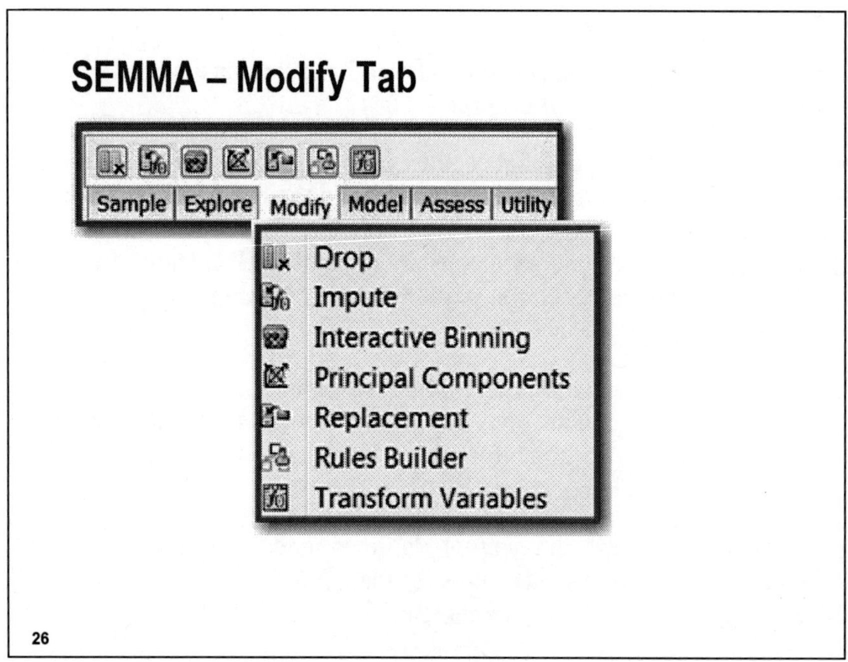


The **Interactive Binning** tool is an interactive grouping tool that you use to model nonlinear functions of multiple modes of continuous distributions. The interactive tool computes initial bins by quantiles, and then you can interactively split and combine the initial bins. You use the Interactive Binning node to create bins (or buckets or classes) of all input variables, which includes both class and interval input variables. You can create bins in order to reduce the number of unique levels as well as attempt to improve the predictive power of each input.

The **Drop** tool is used to remove variables from scored data sets. You can remove all variables with the role type that you specify, or you can manually specify individual variables to drop. For example, you could remove all hidden, rejected, and residual variables from your exported data set, or you could remove just a few variables that you identify yourself.

The **Impute** tool enables you to replace values for observations that have missing values. You can replace missing values for interval variables with the mean, median, midrange, mid-minimum spacing, or distribution-based replacement, or you can use a replacement M-estimator such as Tukey's biweight, Huber's, or Andrew's Wave. You can also estimate the replacement values for each interval input by using a tree-based imputation method. Missing values for class variables can be replaced with the most frequently occurring value, distribution-based replacement, tree-based imputation, or a constant.

The **Principal Components** tool calculates eigenvalues and eigenvectors from the uncorrected covariance matrix, corrected covariance matrix, or the correlation matrix of input variables. Principal components are calculated from the eigenvectors and are usually treated as the new set of input variables for successor modeling tools. A principal components analysis is useful for data interpretation and data dimension reduction.

The **Replacement** tool enables you to reassign and consolidate levels of categorical inputs. This can improve the performance of predictive models.

The **Rules Builder** tool opens the Rules Builder window so that you can create ad hoc sets of rules with user-definable outcomes. You can interactively define the values of the outcome variable and the paths to the outcome. This is useful in ad hoc rule creation such as applying logic for posterior probabilities and scorecard values.

The **Transform Variables** tool enables you to create new variables that are transformations of existing variables in your data. Transformations are useful when you want to improve the fit of a model to the data. For example, transformations can be used to stabilize variances, remove nonlinearity, improve additivity, and correct nonnormality in variables. The Transform Variables tool supports various transformation methods. The available methods depend on the type and the role of a variable.

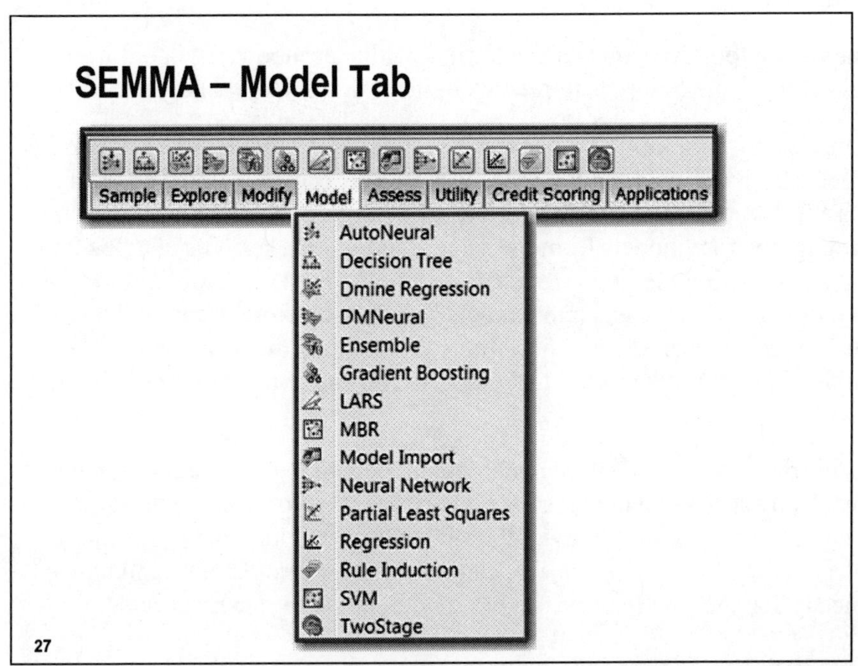


The **AutoNeural** tool can be used to automatically configure a neural network. It conducts limited searches for a better network configuration.

The **Gradient Boosting** tool uses a partitioning algorithm described in "A Gradient Boosting Machine," and "Stochastic Gradient Boosting" by Jerome Friedman. A partitioning algorithm searches for an optimal partition of the data defined in terms of the values of a single variable. The optimality criterion depends on how another variable, the target, is distributed into the partition segments. The more similar the target values are within the segments, the greater the worth of the partition. Most partitioning algorithms further partition each segment in a process called *recursive partitioning*. The partitions are then combined to create a predictive model. The model is evaluated by goodness-of-fit statistics defined in terms of the target variable. These statistics are different than the measure of worth of an individual partition. A good model can result from many mediocre partitions.

The **Decision Tree** tool enables you to perform multiway splitting of your database based on nominal, ordinal, and continuous variables. The tool supports both automatic and interactive training. When you run the Decision Tree tool in automatic mode, it automatically ranks the input variables based on the strength of their contribution to the tree. This ranking can be used to select variables for use in subsequent modeling. In addition, dummy variables can be generated for use in subsequent modeling. You can override any automatic step with the option to define a splitting rule and prune explicit tools or subtrees. Interactive training enables you to explore and evaluate a large set of trees as you develop them.

The **Dmine Regression** tool performs a regression analysis on data sets that have a binary or interval level target variable. The Dmine Regression tool computes a forward stepwise least-squares regression. In each step, an independent variable is selected that contributes maximally to the model R-squared value. The tool can compute all two-way interactions of classification variables, and it also can use AOV16 variables to identify nonlinear relationships between interval variables and the target variable. In addition, the tool can use group variables to reduce the number of levels of classification variables.

If you want to create a regression model on data that contains a nominal or ordinal target, then you would use the Regression tool.

The **DMNeural** tool is another modeling tool that you can use to fit a nonlinear model. The nonlinear model uses transformed principal components as inputs to predict a binary or an interval target variable.

The **Ensemble** tool creates new models by combining the posterior probabilities (for class targets) or the predicted values (for interval targets) from multiple predecessor models. The new model is then used to score new data. One common ensemble approach is to use multiple modeling methods, such as a neural network and a decision tree, to obtain separate models from the same training data set. The component models from the two complementary modeling methods are integrated by the Ensemble tool to form the final model solution. It is important to note that the ensemble model can only be more accurate than the individual models if the individual models disagree with one another. You should always compare the model performance of the ensemble model with the individual models. You can compare models using the Model Comparison tool.

The **LARS** tool can produce models that range from simple intercept models to least square regression models with many input variables. You specify the model selection criteria that you want to use to choose the optimal model. The LARS node sets the role of input variables that were excluded in the optimal model to **Rejected**. Input variables that the LARS node rejects can be passed to subsequent modeling nodes, but their rejected status means that they will not be used as model inputs in successor nodes.

The **Memory-Based Reasoning (MBR)** tool is a modeling tool that uses a *k*-nearest neighbor algorithm to categorize or predict observations. The *k*-nearest neighbor algorithm takes a data set and a probe, where each observation in the data set is composed of a set of variables and the probe has one value for each variable. The distance between an observation and the probe is calculated. The *k* observations that have the smallest distances to the probe are the *k*-nearest neighbors to that probe. In SAS Enterprise Miner, the *k*-nearest neighbors are determined by the Euclidean distance between an observation and the probe. Based on the target values of the *k*-nearest neighbors, each of the *k*-nearest neighbors votes on the target value for a probe. The votes are the posterior probabilities for the class target variable.

The **Model Import** tool imports and assesses a model that was not created by one of the SAS Enterprise Miner modeling nodes. You can then use the Assessment node to compare the user-defined model(s) with a model(s) that you developed with a SAS Enterprise Miner modeling node. This process is called *integrated assessment*.

The **Neural Network** tool enables you to construct, train, and validate multilayer feed-forward neural networks. In general, each input is fully connected to the first hidden layer, each hidden layer is fully connected to the next hidden layer, and the last hidden layer is fully connected to the output. The Neural Network tool supports many variations of this general form.

The **Partial Least Squares** tool models continuous and binary targets based on the PLS procedure in SAS/STAT. The Partial Least Squares node produces DATA step score code and standard predictive model assessment results.

The **Regression** tool enables you to fit both linear and logistic regression models to your data. You can use continuous, ordinal, and binary target variables. You can use both continuous and discrete variables as inputs. The tool supports the stepwise, forward, and backward selection methods. The interface enables you to create higher-order modeling terms such as polynomial terms and interactions.

The **Rule Induction** tool enables you to improve the classification of rare events in your modeling data. It creates a Rule Induction model that uses split techniques to remove the largest pure split tool from the data. Rule Induction also creates binary models for each level of a target variable and ranks the levels from the rarest event to the most common.

A support vector machine (SVM) is a supervised machine learning method that is used to perform classification and regression analysis. Vapnik developed the concept of SVM in terms of hard margin, and later he and his colleague proposed the SVM with slack variables which is a soft margin classifier. The standard SVM problem solves binary classification problems which produce non-probability output (only sign +1/-1) by constructing a set of hyperplanes that maximize the margin between two classes. Most of problems in a finite dimensional space are not linearly separable. In this case, the original space needs to be mapped into a much higher dimensional space or an infinite dimensional space which makes the separation easier. SVM uses a kernel function to define the larger dimensional space.

The SAS Enterprise Miner **SVM** node uses PRCC SVM and PROC SVMSCORE. The tool is located on the Model tab of the Enterprise Miner tool bar. In Enterprise Miner 7.1, the SVM node supports only binary classification problems, including polynomial, radial basis function and sigmoid nonlinear kernels. The SVM node does not support multiclass problems or support vector regression. The frequency variable is ignored.

The **TwoStage** tool enables you to model a class target and an interval target. The interval target variable is usually the value that is associated with a level of the class target. For example, the binary variable **Purchase** is a class target that has two levels, Yes and No, and the interval variable **Amount** can be the value target that represents the amount of money that a customer spends on the purchase.

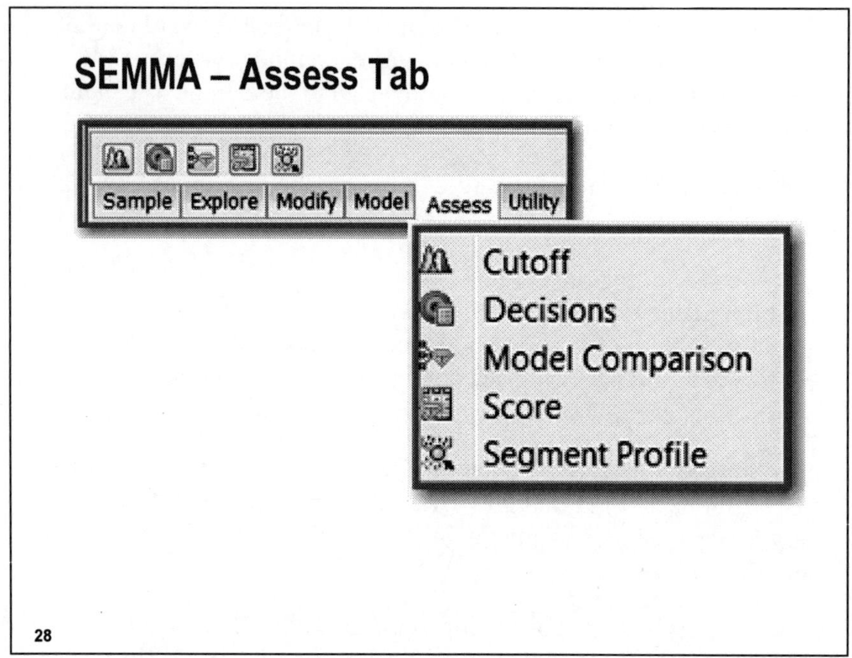


The **Cutoff** tool provides tabular and graphical information to assist users in determining appropriate probability cutoff point(s) for decision making with binary target models. The establishment of a cutoff decision point entails the risk of generating false positives and false negatives, but an appropriate use of the Cutoff node can help minimize those risks.

The **Decisions** tool enables you to define target profiles for a target that produces optimal decisions. The decisions are made using a user-specified decision matrix and output from a subsequent modeling procedure.

The **Model Comparison** tool provides a common framework for comparing models and predictions from any of the modeling tools. The comparison is based on the expected and actual profits or losses that would result from implementing the model. The tool produces several charts that help to describe the usefulness of the model, such as lift charts and profit/loss charts.

The **Segment Profile** tool enables you to examine segmented or clustered data and identify factors that differentiate data segments from the population. The tool generates various reports that aid in exploring and comparing the distribution of these factors within the segments and population.

The **Score** tool enables you to manage, edit, export, and execute scoring code that is generated from a trained model. Scoring is the generating of predicted values for a data set that might not contain a target variable. The Score tool generates and manages scoring formulas in the form of a single SAS DATA step, which can be used in most SAS environments even without the presence of SAS Enterprise Miner. The Score tool can also generate C score code and Java score code.

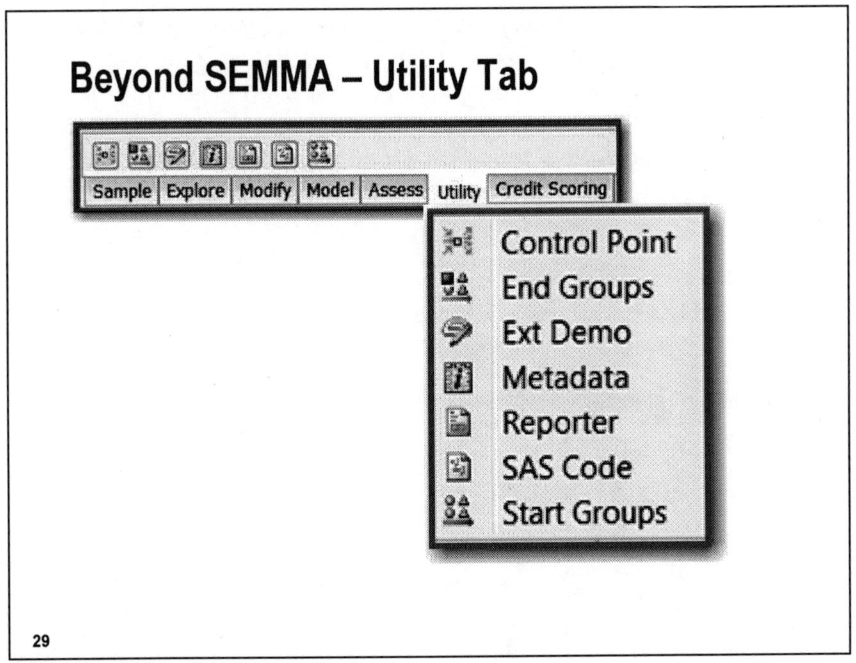


The **Control Point** tool enables you to establish a control point to reduce the number of connections that are made in process flow diagrams. For example, suppose that three Input Data tools are to be connected to three modeling tools. If no Control Point tool is used, then nine connections are required to connect all of the Input Data tools to all of the modeling tools. However, if a Control Point tool is used, only six connections are required.

The **End Groups** tool is used only in conjunction with the Start Groups tool. The End Groups node acts as a boundary marker that defines the end of group processing operations in a process flow diagram. Group processing operations are performed on the portion of the process flow diagram that exists between the Start Groups node and the End Groups node.

The **Ext Demo** tool is designed to illustrate the various property types that can be implemented in SAS Enterprise Miner extension nodes.

The **Metadata** tool enables you to modify column metadata information at some point in your process flow diagram. You can modify attributes such as roles, measurement levels, and order.

The **Reporter** tool uses SAS Output Delivery System (ODS) capability to create a single PDF or RTF file that contains information about the open process flow diagram. The PDF or RTF documents can be viewed and saved directly and are included in SAS Enterprise Miner report package files.

The **SAS Code** tool enables you to incorporate new or existing SAS code into process flow diagrams. The ability to write SAS code enables you to include additional SAS procedures into your data mining analysis. You can also use a SAS DATA step to create customized scoring code, conditionally process data, and concatenate or merge existing data sets. The tool provides a macro facility to dynamically reference data sets used for training, validation, testing, or scoring. Additionally the macro facility can reference variables, such as input, target, and prediction variables. After you run the SAS Code tool, the results and the data sets can then be exported for use by subsequent tools in the diagram.

The **Start Groups** tool is useful when your data can be segmented, or grouped, and you want to process the grouped data in different ways. The Start Groups node uses BY-group processing as a method to process observations from one or more data sources that are grouped or ordered by values of one or more common variables. BY variables identify the variable or variables by which the data source is indexed, and BY statements process data and order output according to the BY group values.

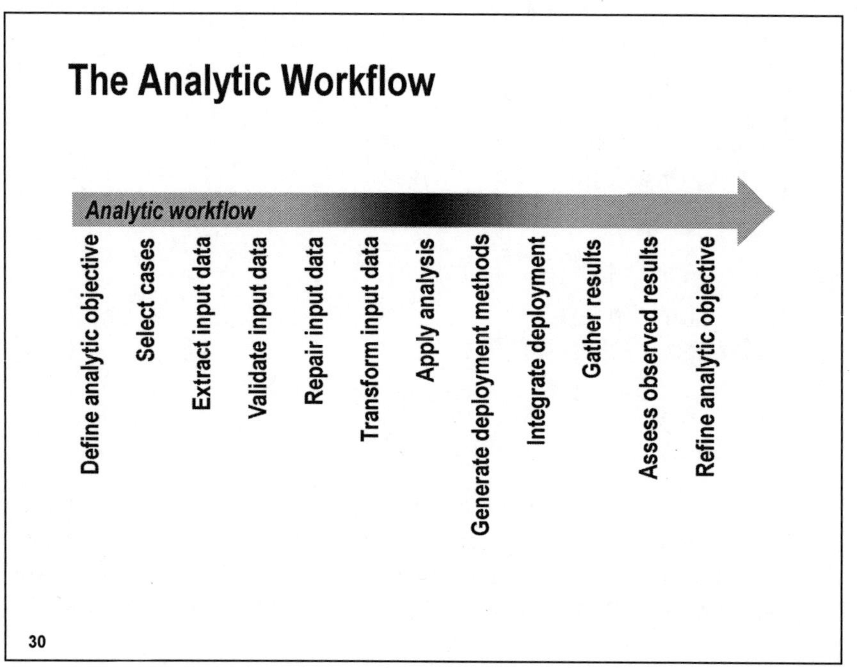


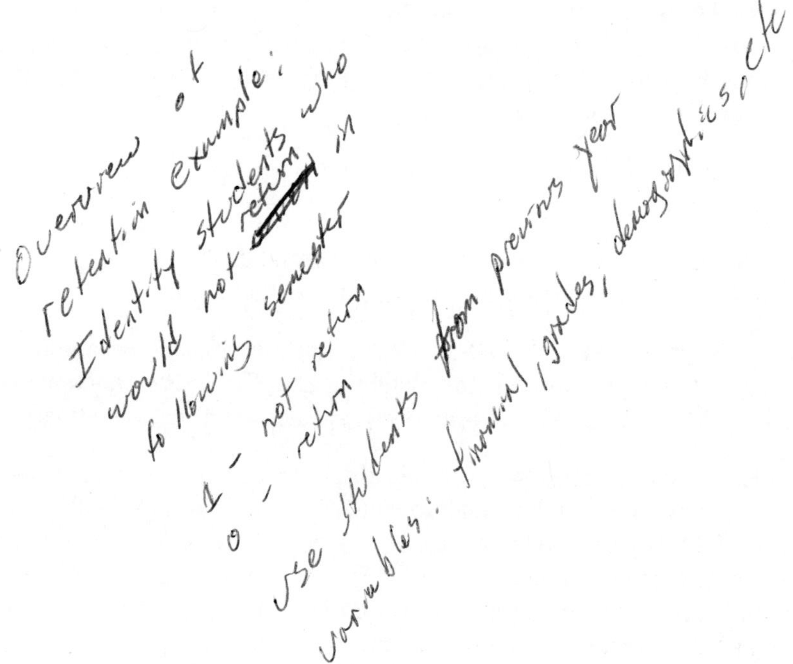

# 1.2 Predictive Modeling Using Enterprise Miner

## Objectives

- Define a SAS data library and write LIBNAME statements.
- Define model roles and measurement levels used in SAS Enterprise Miner.
- Create a data source.
- Conduct initial data exploration.
- Understand the need for data splitting.

32

## SAS Data Libraries

You can think of a SAS data library as a drawer in a filing cabinet and a SAS data set as one of the file folders in the drawer.

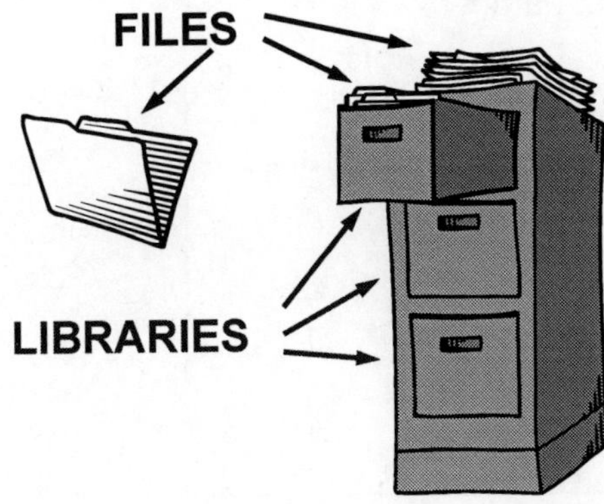


33

## SAS Data Libraries

When you open SAS, you automatically have access to a temporary and a permanent SAS data library.

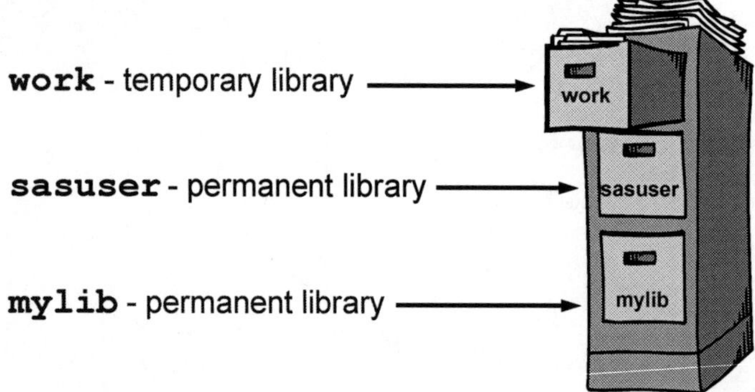


You can create and access your own permanent libraries.

34

The **work** library and its SAS data files are deleted after your SAS session ends. SAS data sets in permanent libraries, such as the **mylib** library, are saved after your SAS session ends.

## Assigning a Libref

You can use SAS code to name a SAS data library.

Rules for naming a library:

- must be eight or fewer characters
- must begin with a letter or underscore
- remaining characters can be letters, numbers, or underscores

You can also do **File** ⇨ **New** ⇨ **Library** to assign a library using the Library Wizard in SAS Enterprise Miner.

35

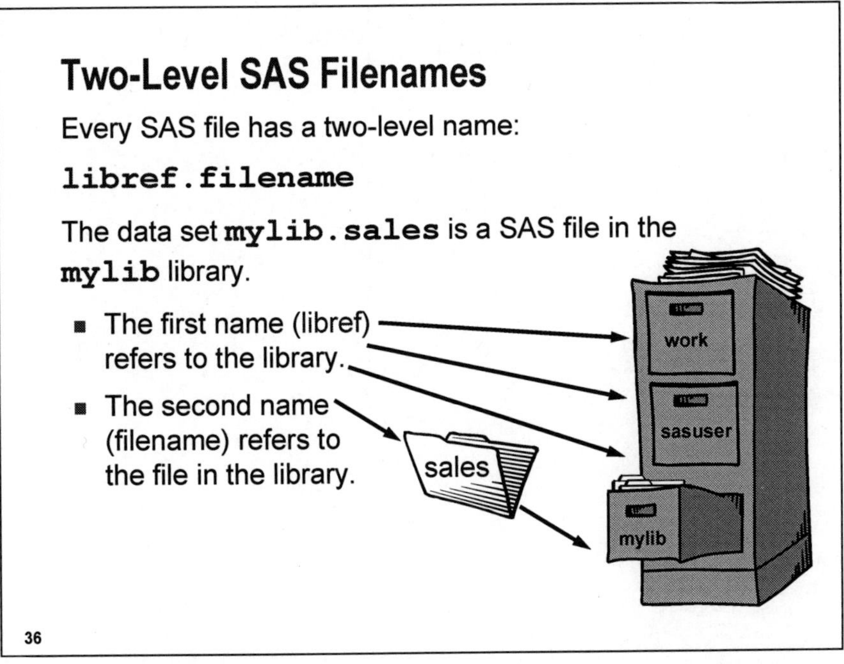

Two-Level SAS Filenames
Every SAS file has a two-level name:
libref.filename
The data set mylib.sales is a SAS file in the mylib library.
The first name (libref) refers to the library.
The second name (filename) refers to the file in the library.
sales
work
sasuser
mylib
36


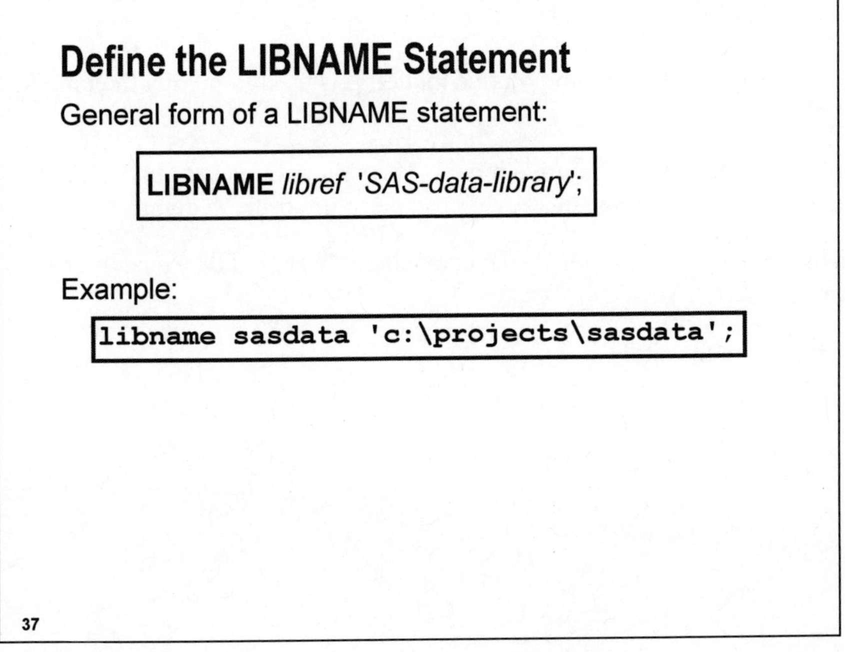

Define the LIBNAME Statement
General form of a LIBNAME statement:
LIBNAME libref 'SAS-data-library';
Example:
libname sasdata 'c:\projects\sasdata';
37


In SAS Enterprise Miner, you can use a LIBNAME statement to assign a libref in the startup code or in a SAS Code node. As an alternative to writing a LIBNAME statement, you can use the Library Wizard in SAS Enterprise Miner.

## Model Roles

A *model role* defines the function of a variable in an analysis. Some of the model roles used in SAS Enterprise Miner are as follows:

- Input
- Target
- ID
- Rejected

38

There are many model roles available in SAS Enterprise Miner. Here are some of the more commonly used roles that are addressed in this course:

| | |
|---|---|
| Input | the independent or explanatory variable in a predictive model. It is used to predict the target variable. |
| Target | the dependent or response variable in a predictive model. The value of this variable is known in some currently available data but will be unknown in some future or fresh data. |
| ID | an identification variable for each observation in the data table. This could be a customer or account number or name. |
| Rejected | a variable that is excluded from the analysis. |

## Measurement Levels

A *measurement level* describes the amount of information contained in the data. The measurement levels used by SAS Enterprise Miner are as follows:

- Unary
- Binary
- Nominal
- Ordinal
- Interval

39

Measurement levels often determine how a variable will be coded in an analysis or shown in a graph. The measurement levels in SAS Enterprise Miner are as follows:

Unary contains one discrete value.

Binary contains two discrete values.

Nominal contains a discrete set of more than two values. The values have no logical ordering.

Ordinal contains a discrete set of more than two values that have a logical ordering.

Interval contains values that vary across a continuous range. The relative distances between the values are meaningful.

## The Scenario

Churn refers to the tendency of a subscriber to switch providers; it is one of the most common problems faced globally in the telecommunication industry. Reasons why a customer might churn include a competitive stimulation, unhappiness with service after the sale, dissatisfaction with quality of services, a move to another location, or disconnection by the provider due to account delinquency. The objective of this analysis is to build a classification model quickly and easily to measure the propensity for an active customer to churn. This enables service agents to take proactive steps to retain targeted profitable customers before churn occurs. .

40

# Initial Data Exploration

## Opening SAS Enterprise Miner

1. To begin, select **Start** ⇨ **All Programs** ⇨ **SAS** ⇨ **Analytics** ⇨ **SAS Enterprise Miner 7.1** This opens the SAS Analytics Platform window.

2. Enter the appropriate user name and password, and then select **Log On**. The Welcome to Enterprise Miner Window opens.

## Setting Up the Initial Project and Diagram

1. Select **New Project...** in the Welcome to Enterprise Miner window.

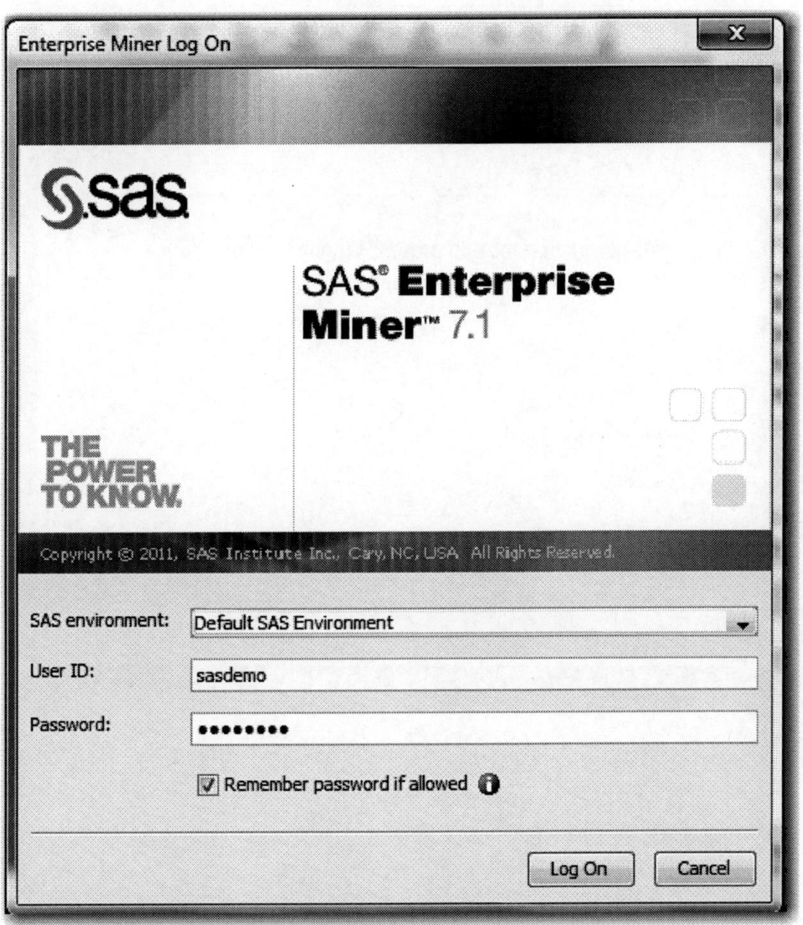

2. Type the name of the project (for example, **Churn**) and the location of the project folder (for example, **C:\WORKSHOP\WINSAS**).

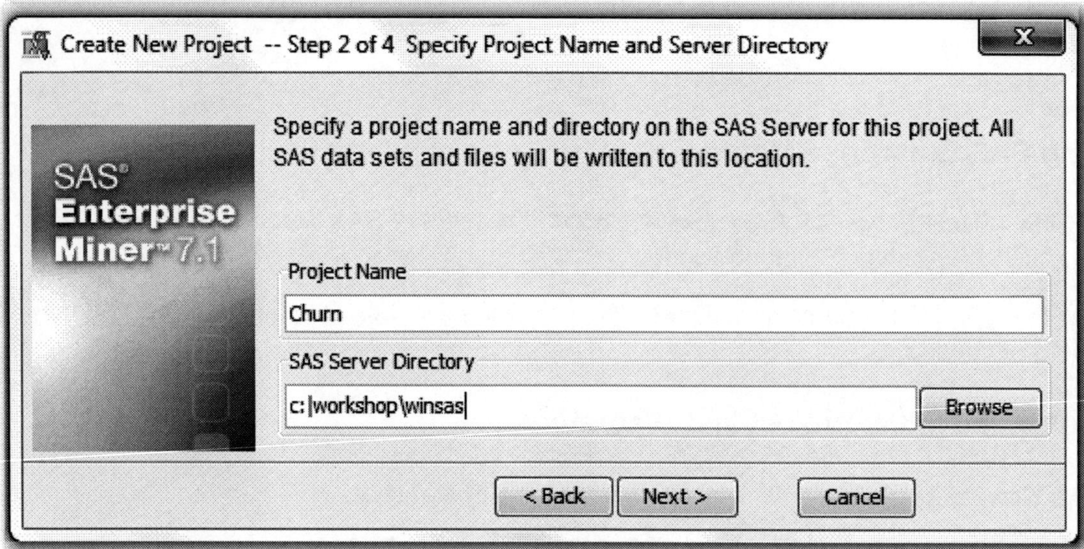


3. Select Next >.

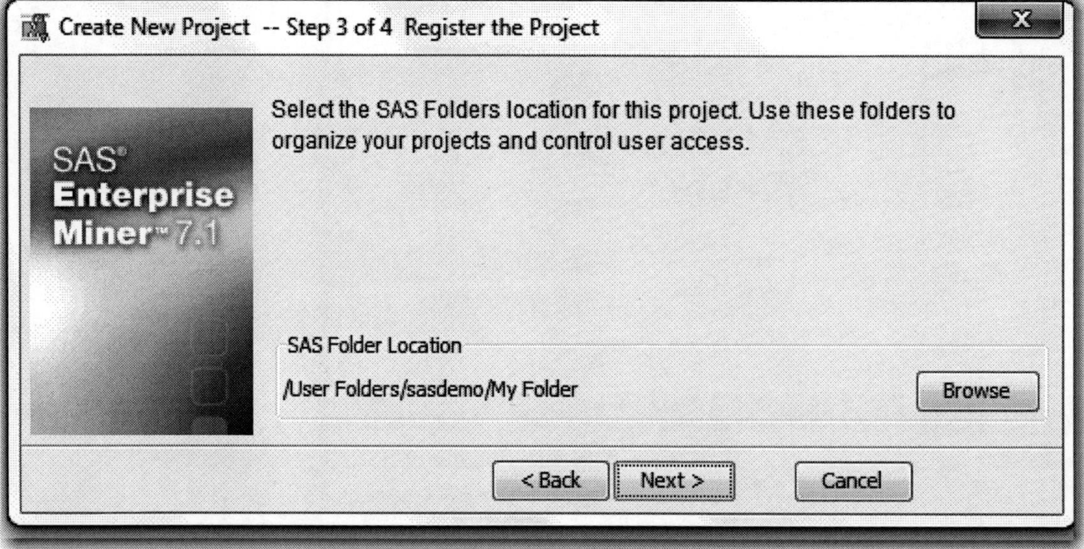


4. Accept the default folder location.

5. Select Next >.

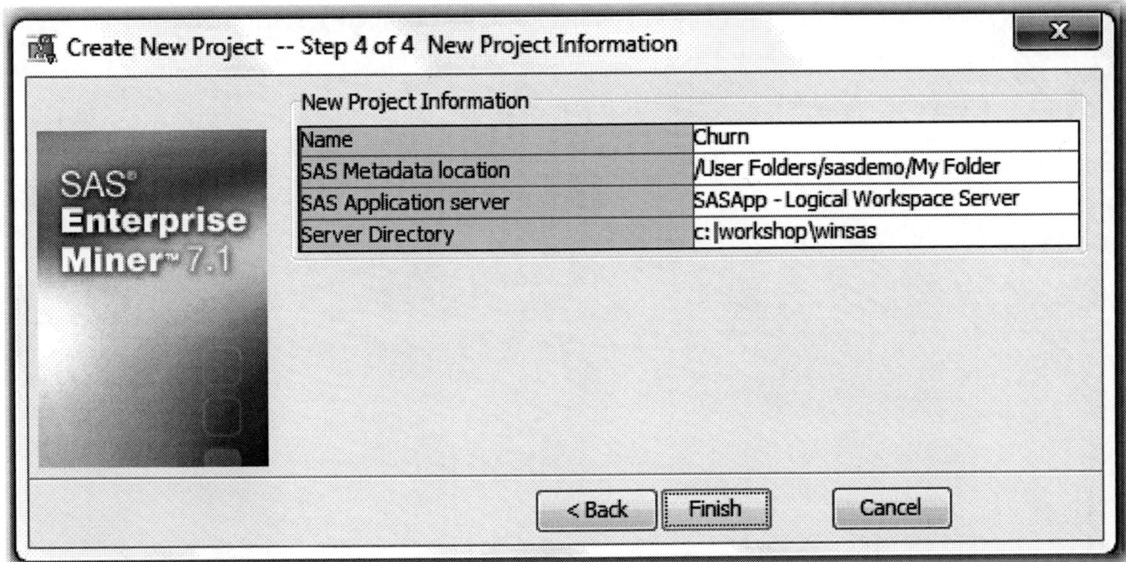


6. Select Finish.

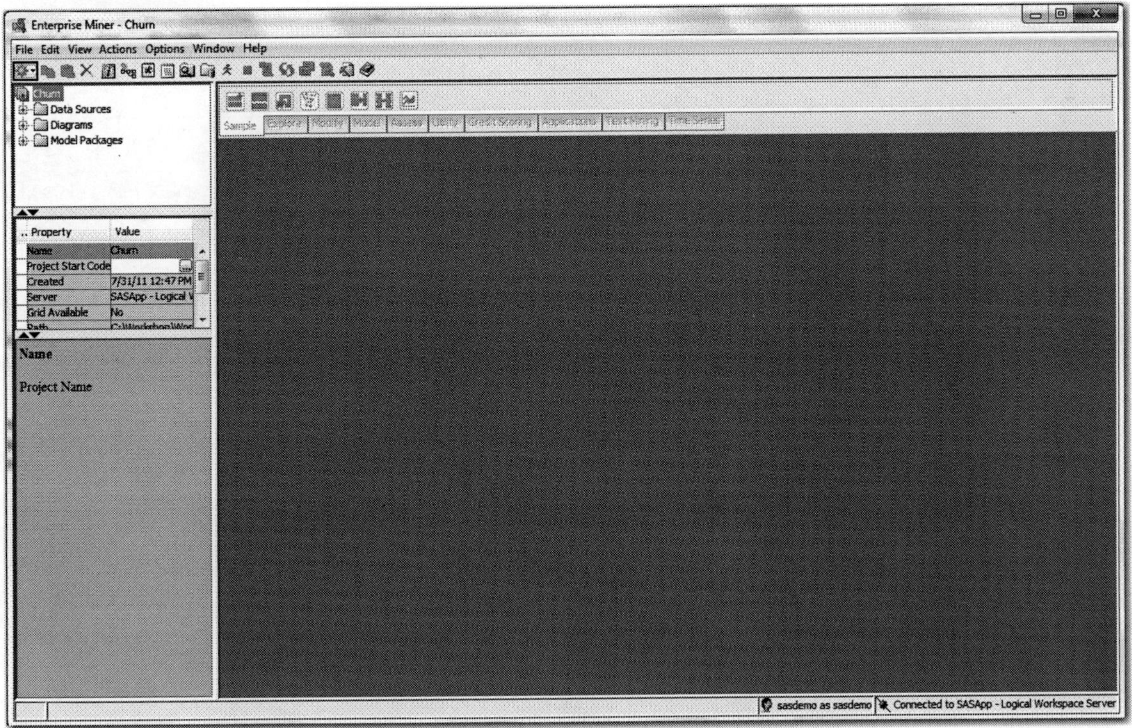


7. Select the button associated with Project Start Code.

8. A window opens that enables you to enter commands to be executed at startup of a project. Type the LIBNAME statement for this project:

   **libname Churn 'C:\workshop\winsas\Garpm\data';**

   Or you could do **File** ⇨ **New** ⇨ **Library** and use the Library Wizard to define the library.

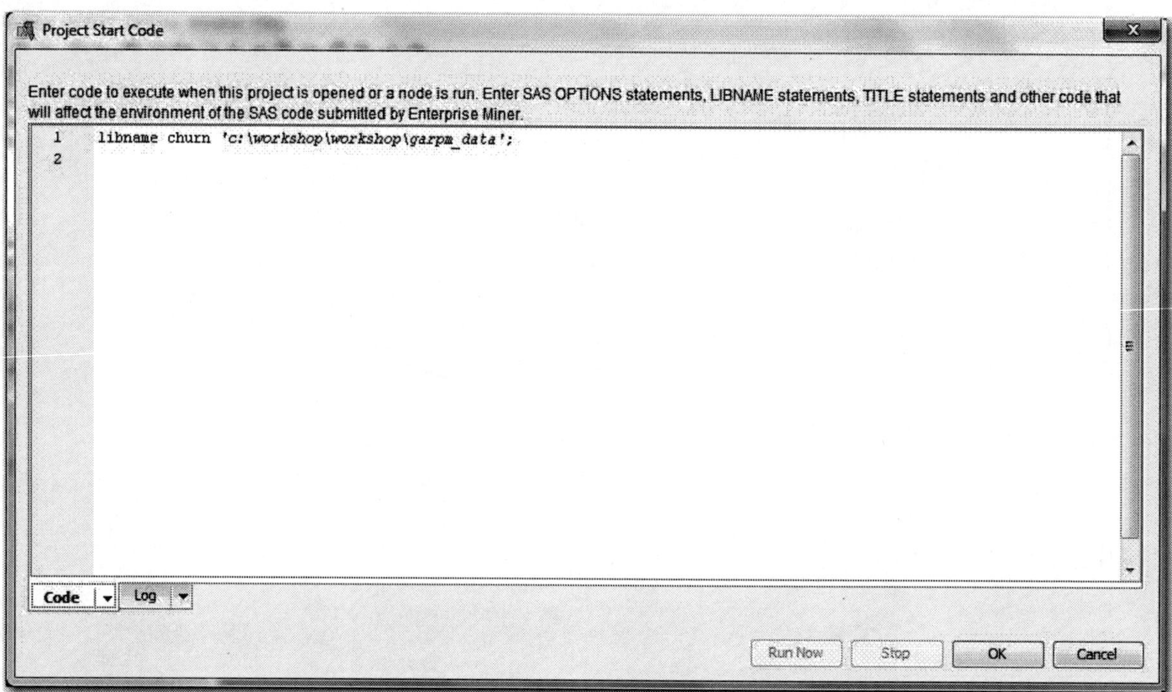


9. Select Run Now and then OK.

   ✎ It is necessary to include the library definition in the project startup code. Including the LIBNAME statement here ensures that the library is defined for every diagram and node in the project and that SAS will find the data.

10. To build a diagram to work in, select **File** ⇨ **New** ⇨ **Diagram….**

11. Type the diagram name, for example, **Diagram 1**.

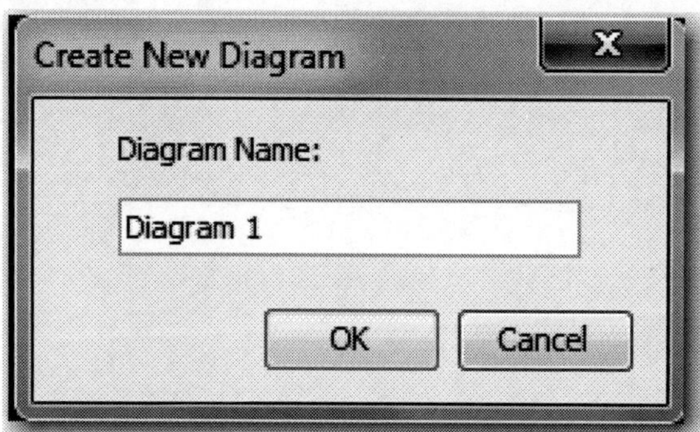


12. Select OK. The diagram workspace is open and ready to use.

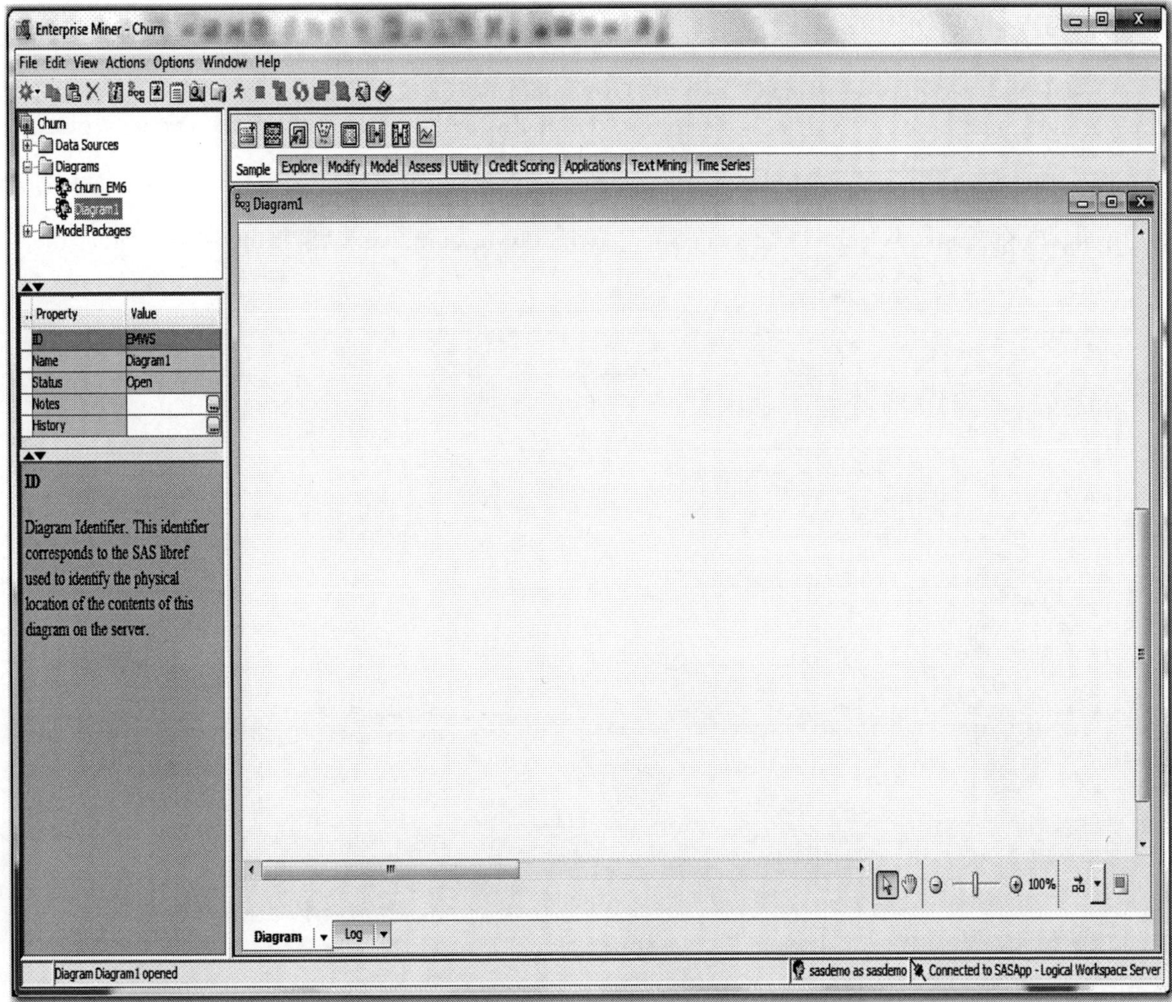
Enterprise Miner - Churn
File Edit View Actions Options Window Help
Churn
Data Sources
Diagrams
churn_EM6
Diagram1
Model Packages
Sample
Explore
Modify
Model
Assess
Utility
Credit Scoring
Applications
Text Mining
Time Series
Diagram1
Property
Value
ID
EMWS
Name
Diagram1
Status
Open
Notes
History
ID
Diagram Identifier. This identifier corresponds to the SAS libref used to identify the physical location of the contents of this diagram on the server.
100%
Diagram
Log
Diagram Diagram1 opened
sasdemo as sasdemo
Connected to SASApp - Logical Workspace Server

## Defining a Data Source

The **CHURN_RPM** data set in the **Churn** library contains 4,708 observations for building and comparing competing models. The first step is to define this data set as a data source for the project.

1. To define a data source, right-click **Data Sources** in the Project panel and select **Create Data Source**.
2. In the Data Source Wizard - Metadata Source window, be sure that **SAS Table** is selected as the source and select Next >.

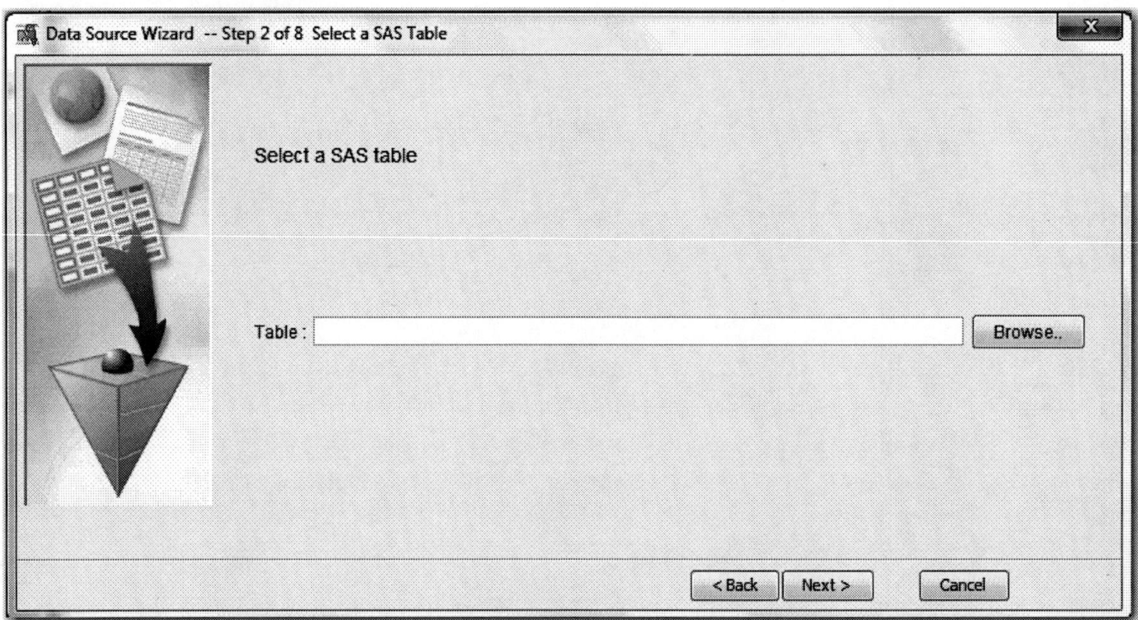


3. To choose the desired data table, select Browse...

4. Double-click **Churn** to see the datasets in the **Churn** library.

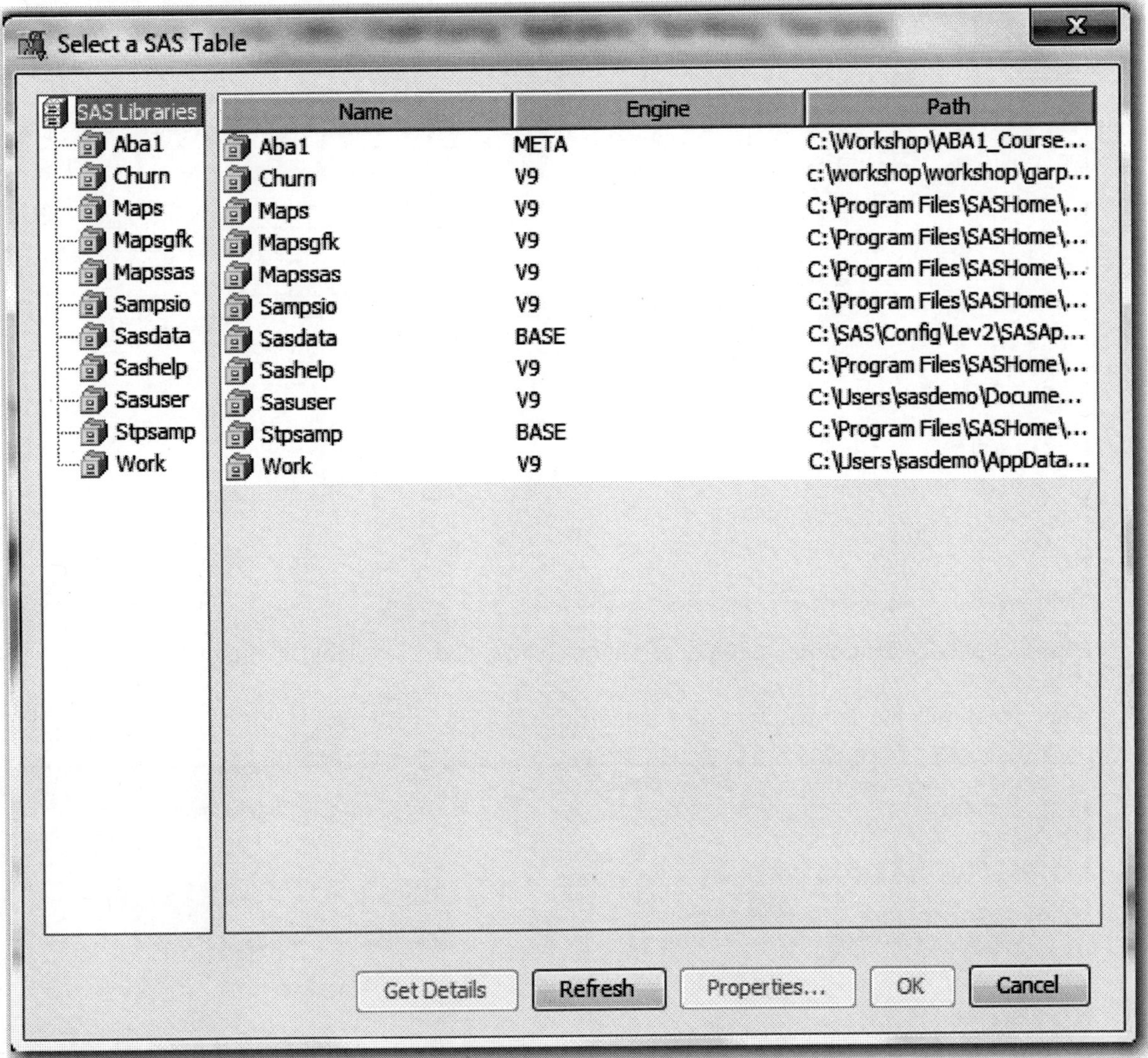


5. Select **Churn_RPM**, and then select OK.

6. Select Next >.

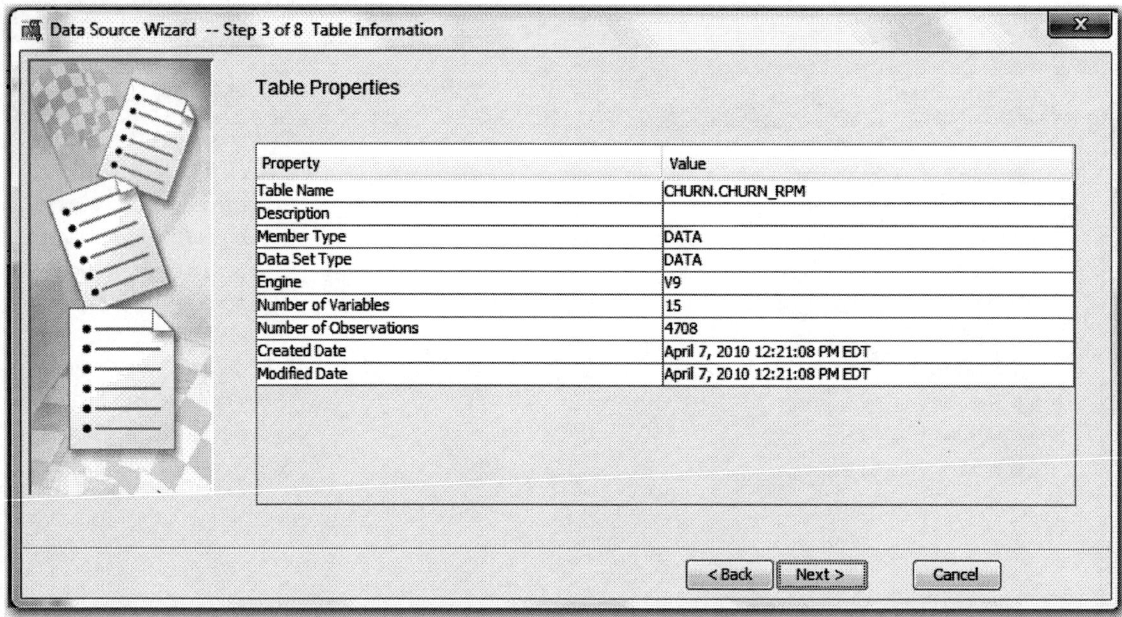


| Property | Value |
|---|---|
| Table Name | CHURN.CHURN_RPM |
| Description | |
| Member Type | DATA |
| Data Set Type | DATA |
| Engine | V9 |
| Number of Variables | 15 |
| Number of Observations | 4708 |
| Created Date | April 7, 2010 12:21:08 PM EDT |
| Modified Date | April 7, 2010 12:21:08 PM EDT |

Observe that this dataset has 4,708 observations (rows) and 15 variables (columns).

7. After examining the dataset properties, select Next >.

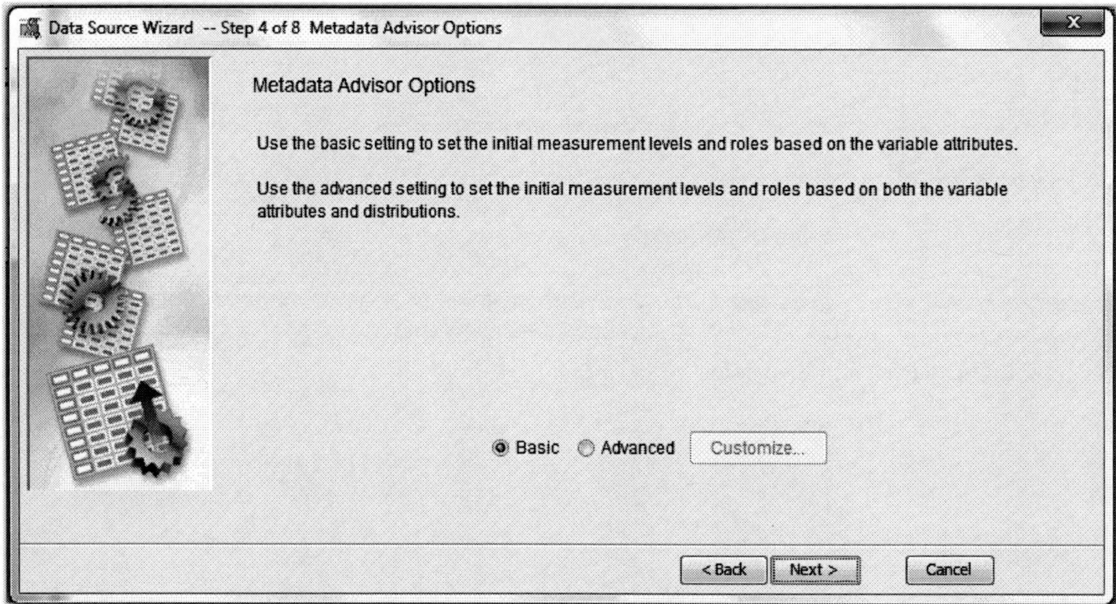


All analysis packages must determine how to use variables in the analysis. If you choose the Basic option here, the initial role and level of the variables will be determined by the variable type and format values. If you choose the **Advanced** option here, initial roles and levels are based on the variable type, format values, and the number of distinct values contained in the variable.

8. Select **Advanced** to use the **Advanced** advisor to initially determine the roles and levels for the variables.

9. Select Customize... to view the details of the options that are available.

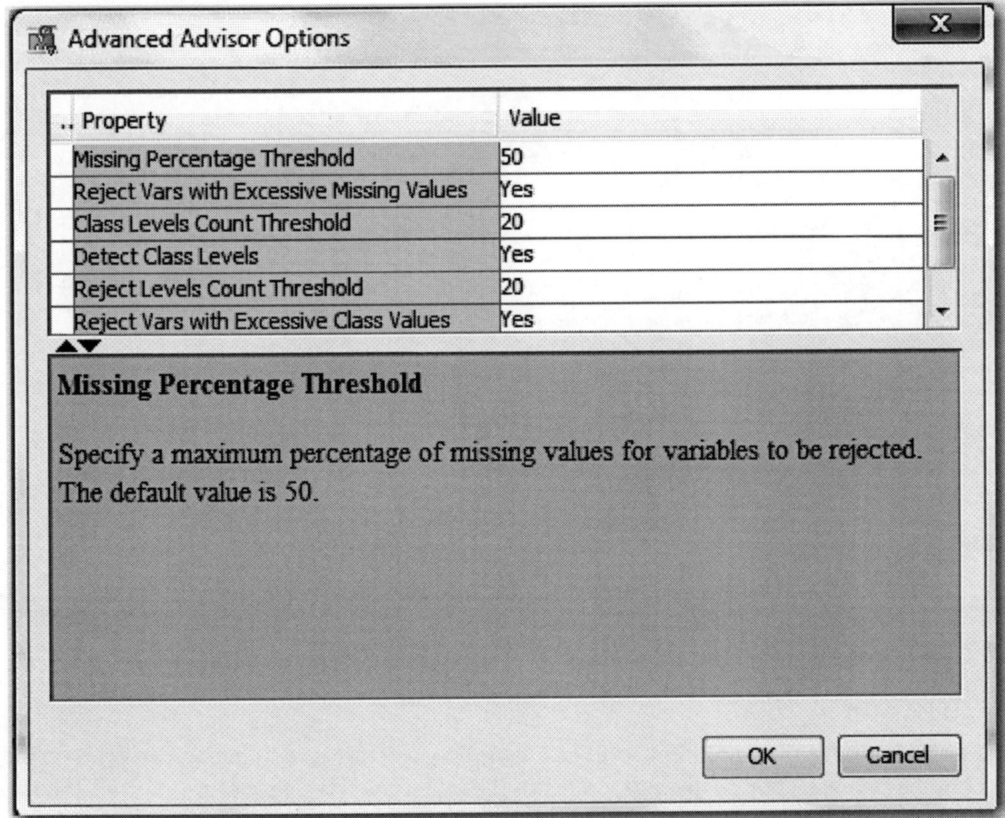


The first two choices address the number of missing values in a variable. The default settings are to reject variables that have more than 50% of their values missing. The next two choices address numeric variables. The default setting is that numeric variables with fewer than 20 unique values are assigned as nominal variables. Finally, the last two choices address the maximum number of levels in a character variable. Any character variable with more than 20 levels is rejected. You can override all of the decisions made by these rules when you examine the column metadata.

10. To leave the default values in place, select Cancel.

11. Select Next >.

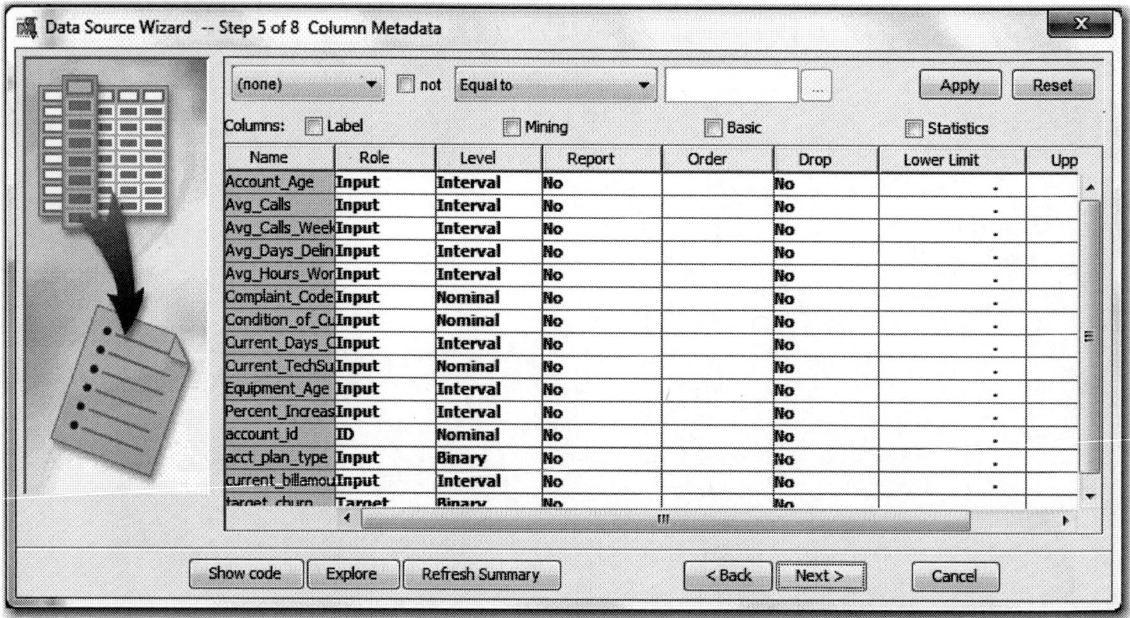

Observe that some of the columns are grayed out. These columns represent information from the SAS data set that cannot be changed with the Data Source Wizard.

The most variables have the measurement level **Interval** because they are numeric variables in the SAS data set and have more than 20 distinct values in the data table. The model role for all interval variables is set to **Input** by default.

The numeric variables with less than 20 values have been assigned **Nominal** as the measurement level. The model role for all binary variables is set to **Input** by default. The variable **ID** has been assigned the role of **ID** and a measurement level of **Nominal**. Character variables are assigned a measurement level of **Nominal**. Since the variable **Target_churn** has target in its' name it is assigned the role of **Target** and since it has only two values level is **Binary**.

### Inspecting Distributions

You can inspect the distribution of values for each of the variables. To view the distribution of the target variable:

1. Select the row for **Target_churn**.
2. Select Explore.
3. Examine the Sample Properties window.

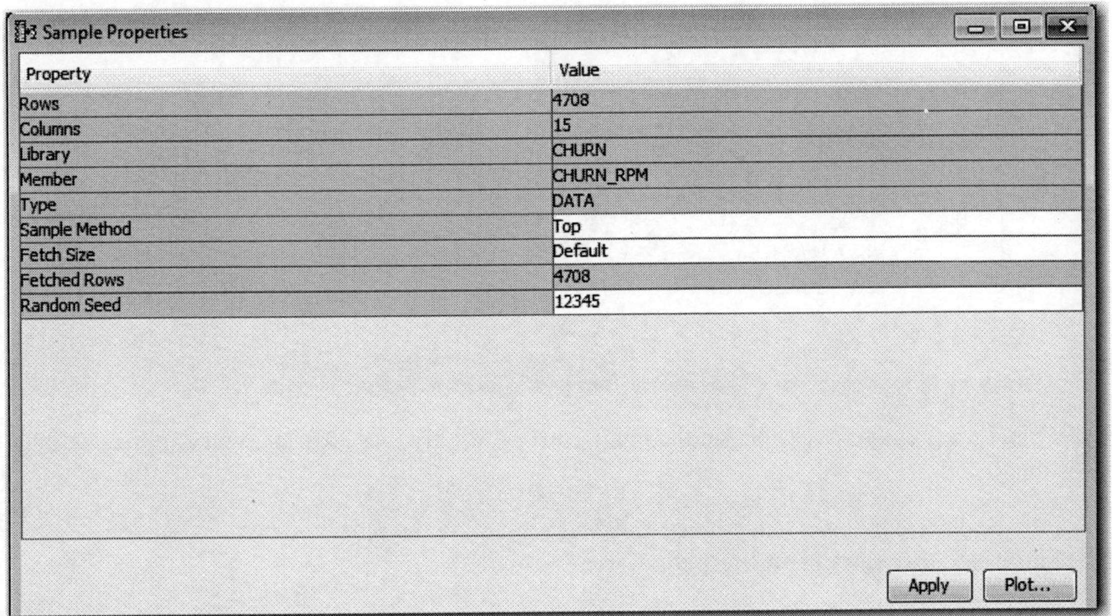

Sample Properties

| Property | Value |
|---|---|
| Rows | 4708 |
| Columns | 15 |
| Library | CHURN |
| Member | CHURN_RPM |
| Type | DATA |
| Sample Method | Top |
| Fetch Size | Default |
| Fetched Rows | 4708 |
| Random Seed | 12345 |



By default, the number of rows used in the exploration of variables depends on the record length and the number of rows in the data table. When the data table is large, fewer rows are selected, or fetched, for use. Presuming that all rows are not used for variable exploration, the top rows are selected by default. You can control this behavior by changing the sample method. After a particular sample method has been selected, you can determine how large a sample you want to use for exploration purposes. In this case, all of the rows are fetched, so no changes are necessary. You can also change the fetch size to Max, but in this case it does matter since there are only 4708 observations. Max fetch size is usually close to 20,000 observations.

4. Examine the bar chart for **Target_churn**.

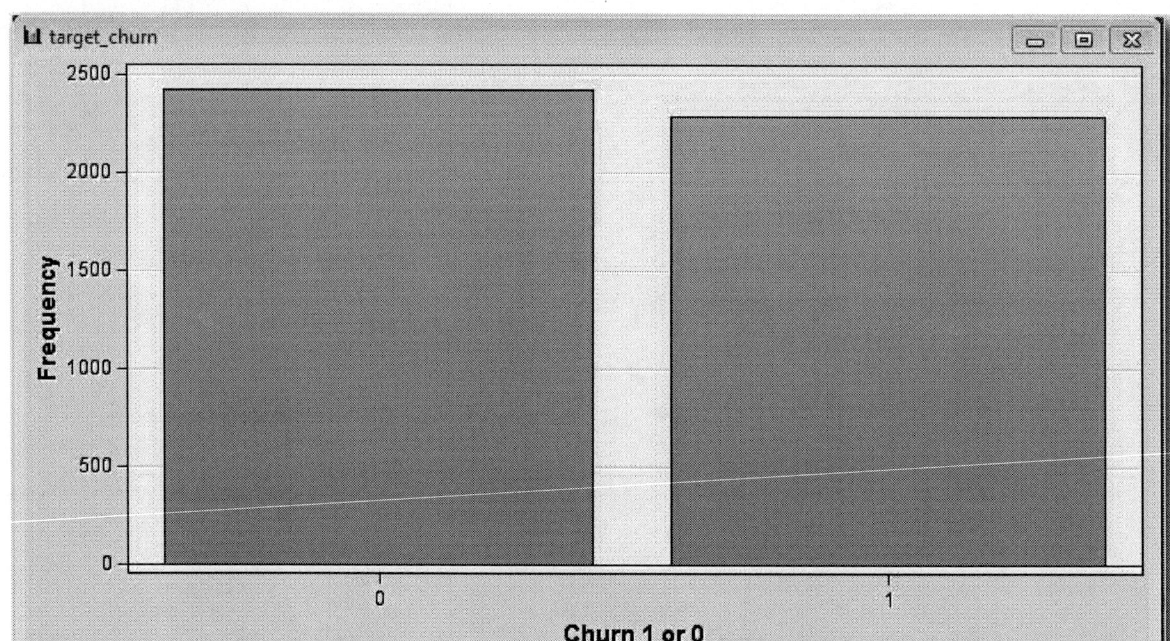


If you place your cursor over a bar in the chart, the specific frequency of the value represented by that bar is displayed.

Close the Explore window when you are finished inspecting the plot. You can evaluate the distribution of other variables as desired.

5. When you finish exploring the distribution of the variables, return to the Data Source Wizard - Column Metadata window.

## Understanding Decision Processing for a Binary Target

When building predictive models, the "best" model often varies according to the criteria used for evaluation. One criterion might suggest that the best model is the one that most accurately predicts the response. Another criterion might suggest that the best model is the one that generates the highest expected profit. These criteria can lead to quite different results.

In SAS Enterprise Miner, you can configure the decisions to be based on profits and losses associated with different types of errors.

In addition to considering the ramifications of different types of errors, it is important to consider whether the sample is representative of the population. If your sample is not representative of the population, you can specify the prior probabilities (the "known" population response rate). This ensures that you obtain appropriate predicted values from your model.

In the case of rare target events, it is not uncommon to oversample. This is because you tend to get better models when they are built on a data set that is more balanced with respect to the levels of the target variable. Our data is oversampled; the probabilities in the population are 4% churners and 96% non-churners.

When building predictive models, the choice of the "best" model depends on the criteria you use to compare competing models. SAS Enterprise Miner enables you to specify information about the target that can be used to compare competing models. To generate a target profile for a variable, you must have already set the model role for the variable to target. This analysis does not require any changes to the default decision processing.

1. Select Next > to continue with the data source definition.

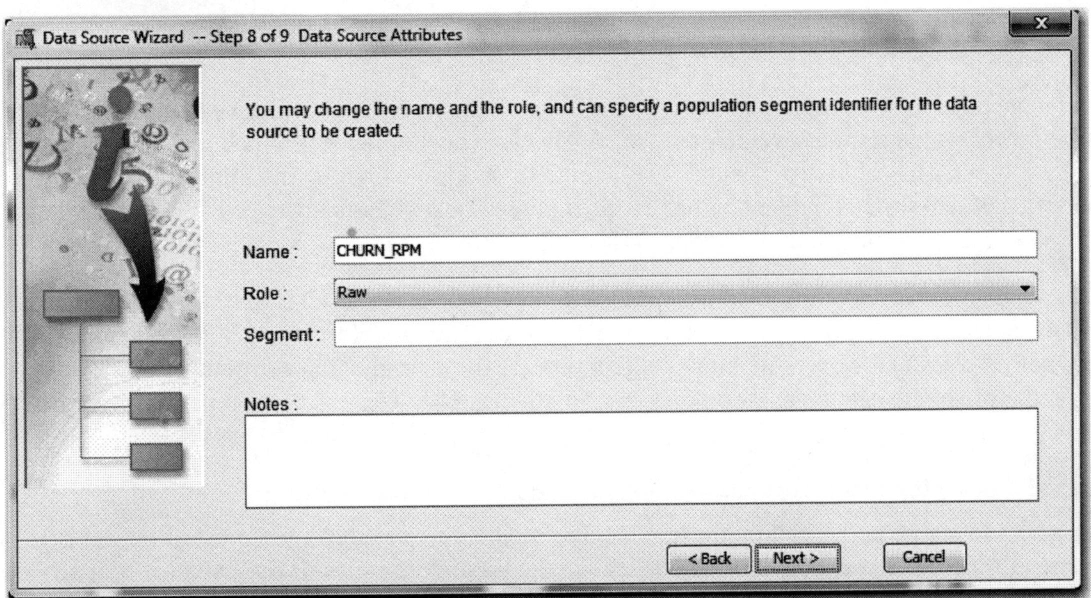


If you want, you can add notes about the data set, and then select Next >. A dialog window opens that provides a summary of the metadata.

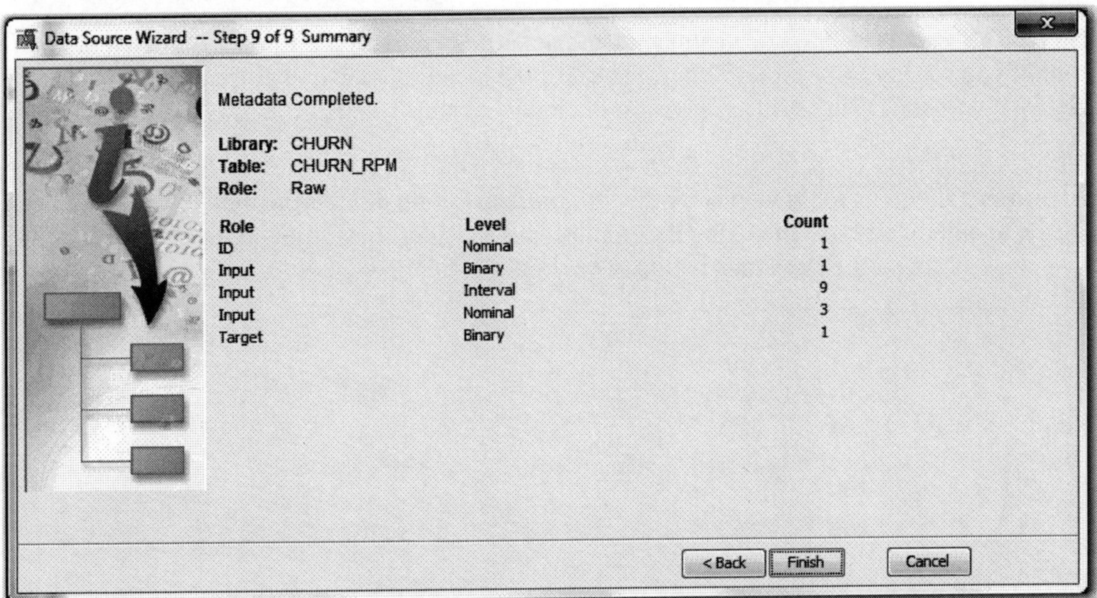


2. Select Finish. The **Churn_RPM** data set has been added as a data source for this project.

### Adjusting for Oversampling (Separate Sampling)

A common predictive modeling practice is to build models from a sample with a primary outcome proportion different from the true population proportion. This is typically done when the ratio of primary to secondary outcome cases is small.

Separate sampling gets its name from the technique used to generate the modeling data, that is, samples are drawn separately based on the target outcome. In the case of a rare primary outcome, usually all primary outcome cases are selected. Then, each primary outcome case is matched by one or (optimally) more secondary outcome cases.

The advantage of separate sampling is that you are able to obtain (on the average) a model of similar predictive power with a smaller overall case count. This is in concordance with the idea that the amount of information in a data set with a categorical outcome is determined not by the total number of cases in the data set itself, but instead by the number of cases in the rarest outcome category. (For binary target data sets, this is usually the primary outcome.) (Harrell 2006)

This advantage might seem of minimal importance in the age of extremely fast computers. (A model might fit 10 times faster with a reduced data set, but a 10-second model fit versus a 1-second model fit is probably not relevant.) However, the model-fitting process occurs only after the completion of a long, tedious, and error-prone data preparation process. Smaller sample sizes for data preparation are usually welcome.

While it reduces analysis time, separate sampling also introduces some analysis complications.

- Most model fit statistics (especially those related to prediction decisions) and most of the assessment plots are closely tied to the outcome proportions in the training samples. If the outcome proportions in the training and validation samples do not match the outcome proportions in the scoring population, model performance can be greatly misestimated.
- If the outcome proportions in the training sample and scoring populations do not match, model prediction estimates are biased.

Fortunately, SAS Enterprise Miner can adjust assessments and prediction estimates to match the scoring population if you specify *prior probabilities*, the scoring population outcome proportions. This is precisely what was done using the Decisions option in the demonstration.

The prior probabilities in the population for our churn data was .04 for churners and .96 for non-churners. Enterprise Miner allows us to provide enter this information before or after the modeling is complete. We have chosen to enter it after the modeling is complete and we enter it by going to the data node and in the property panels selecting the **Decisions** button. The resulting dialog window is shown below.

## Building the Initial Flow and Setting Prior Probabilities

1. Presuming that **Diagram 1** in the project is open; add the **Data Source** node for the **Churn_RPM** data source to the workspace. To accomplish this, first expand **Data Sources** in the project panel, and then drag the **Churn_RPM** data source icon onto the diagram workspace.

2. In the property panel select the ellipse button for **Decisions**.

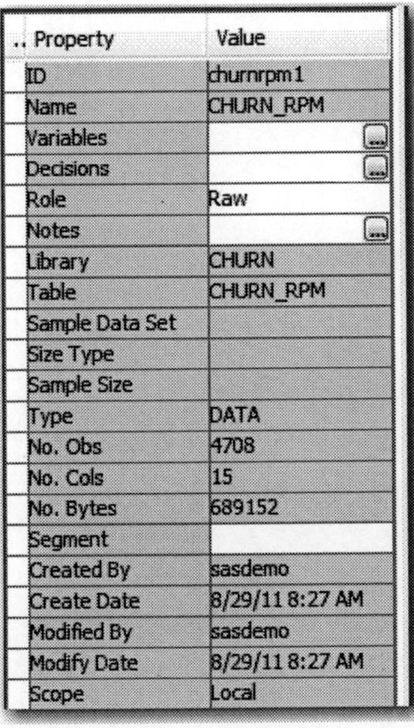

| .. Property | Value |
|---|---|
| ID | churnrpm1 |
| Name | CHURN_RPM |
| Variables | |
| Decisions | |
| Role | Raw |
| Notes | |
| Library | CHURN |
| Table | CHURN_RPM |
| Sample Data Set | |
| Size Type | |
| Sample Size | |
| Type | DATA |
| No. Obs | 4708 |
| No. Cols | 15 |
| No. Bytes | 689152 |
| Segment | |
| Created By | sasdemo |
| Create Date | 8/29/11 8:27 AM |
| Modified By | sasdemo |
| Modify Date | 8/29/11 8:27 AM |
| Scope | Local |

3. The dialog window below appears; now select **Build ⇨ Prior Probabilities** then select **Yes** and enter .04 and .96 as indicated in the dialog window below..

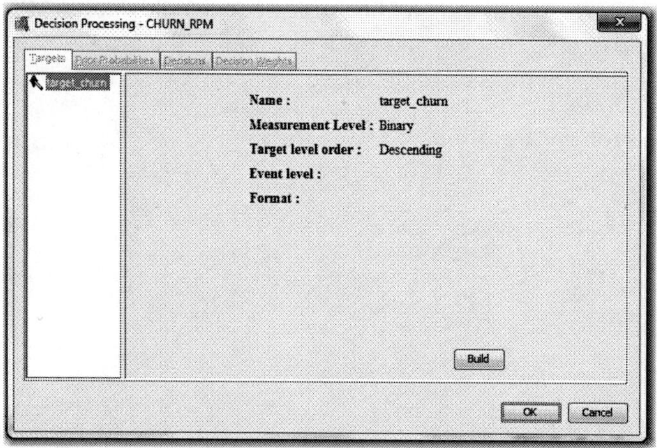


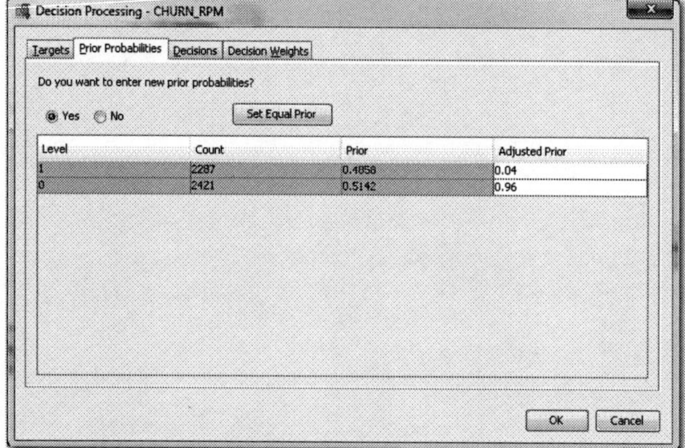


4. Select the tab labeled "**Decisions**" and then select **Yes** and the button labeled "**Defaults With Inverse Prior Weights**".

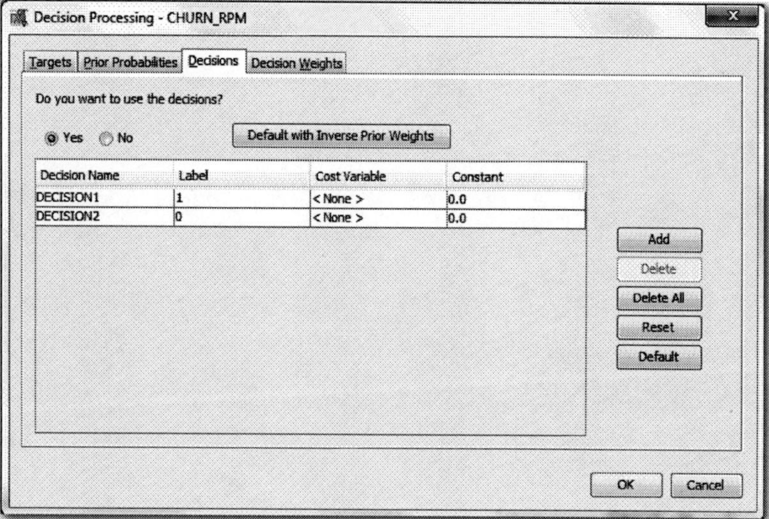

5 Selecting the Decision Weights tab shows that the inverse weights are 25 for Decision1 and 1.0416667 for Decision2, this changes the cutoff of probabilities to be .04. This option is chosen since the probability of churn is small.

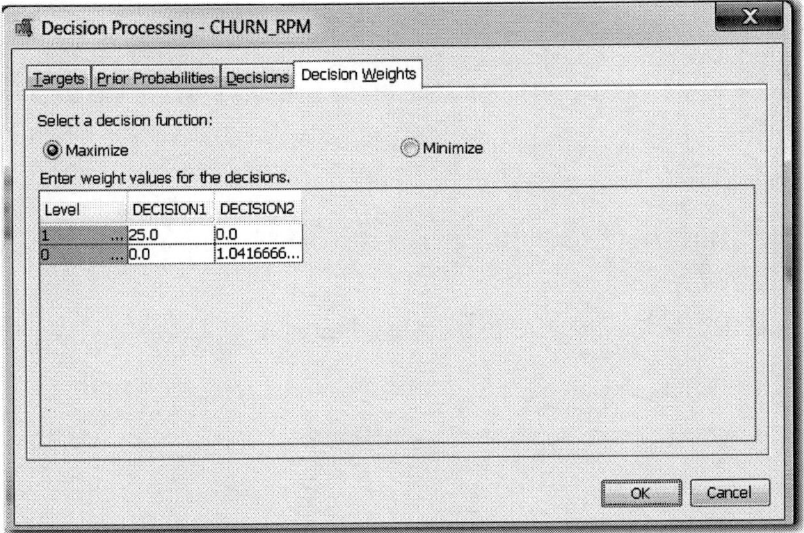


6. Select the **Explore** tab in the toolbar and drag a **MultiPlot** node to the workspace to the right of the **Churn_rpm** data source node. Your diagram should appear as shown below.

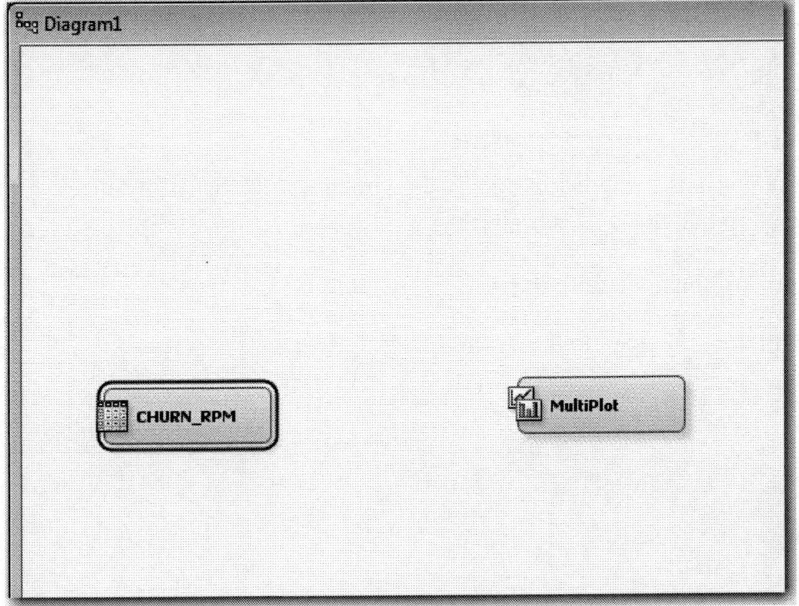


Observe that the **Churn_RPM** node is selected (as indicated by the outline around it), but the **MultiPlot** node is not selected. If you click in any open space on the workspace, both nodes become deselected.

In addition to dragging a node onto the workspace, there is another way to add a node to the flow. You can right-click in the workspace where you want the node to be placed and select **Add node** from the pop-up menu. An additional pop-up menu appears, enabling you to select the desired node.

The shape of the cursor changes depending on where it is positioned. The behavior of the mouse commands depends on the shape as well as the selection state of the node over which the cursor is positioned.

To connect the two nodes in the workspace:

1. Position the cursor on the edge of the right side of the icon representing the **Churn_RPM** data source (until the pencil appears).
2. Click the left mouse button and drag in the direction of the **MultiPlot** node.
3. Release the mouse button after reaching the left edge of the icon that represents the **MultiPlot** node.

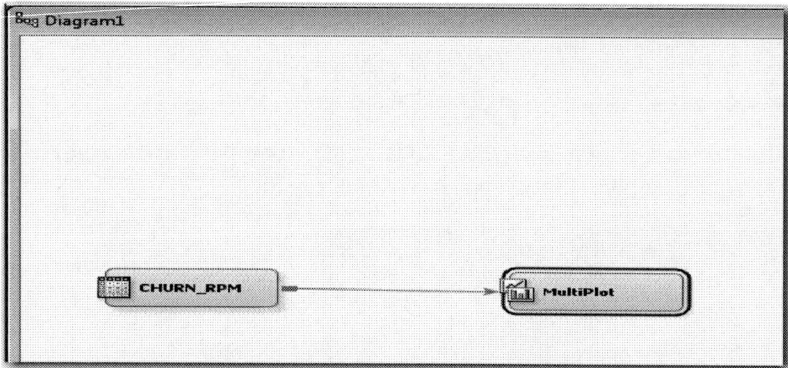


Observe that when you put your cursor in the middle of a node, the cursor appears as a four-headed arrow, ✥ . You would follow these steps to move the nodes around the workspace:

1. Position the cursor in the middle of the node until the arrows appear.
2. Click the left mouse button and drag the node to the desired location.
3. Release the left mouse button.

## Additional Data Exploration

There are several tools available in SAS Enterprise Miner that enables you to explore your data further. One such tool is the **MultiPlot** node. The **MultiPlot** node creates a series of histograms and bar charts that enable you to examine the relationships between the input variables and the binary target variable.

1. Right-click on the **MultiPlot** node and select **Run**.
2. When prompted, select Yes to run the path.
3. When the run has completed, select Results... to view the results.

   The **Output** window of the results displays a summary of the variables in the data table and then some descriptive statistics for the class variables and the interval variables.

   In the **SAS Graphs** window of the results, you can use the Next > button to view the histograms generated for this data. You can also move to a specific graph using the drop-down menu.

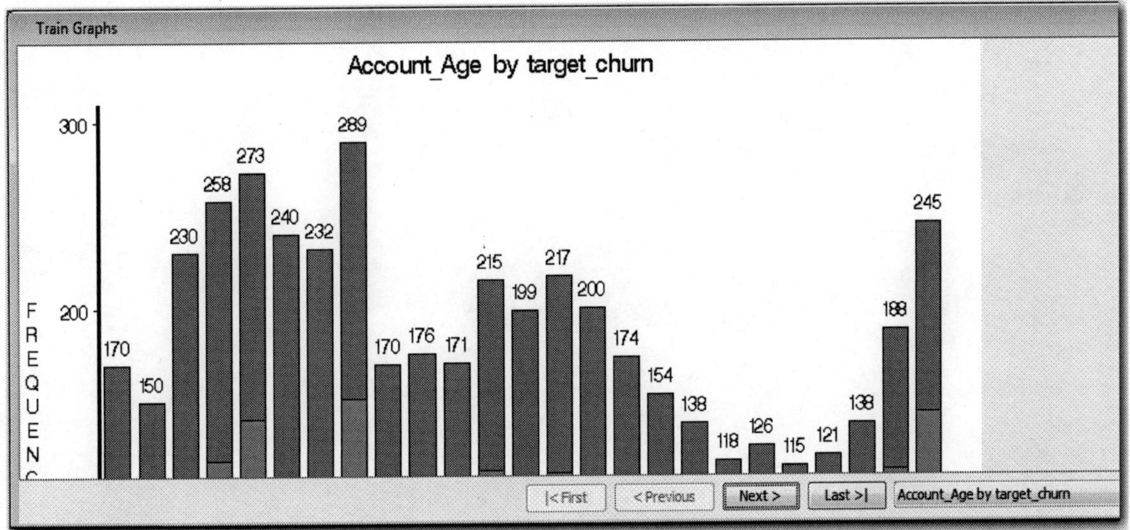


   From this histogram, you can see stacked bar charts for values of age. This gives you a visual representation of the relationship between **Account_Age** and the target variable. Selecting the next button will advance to the next plot.

   Another node used to explore data is the **StatExplore** node. It can be used to examine the distributions of variables in the data set. In addition, the node can be used to select variables to be used in future analyses, such as predictive models. In this case, you would like to examine the distributions of the variables.

4. Add a **StatExplore** node to the workspace and connect it to the **Churn_RPM** data source node.

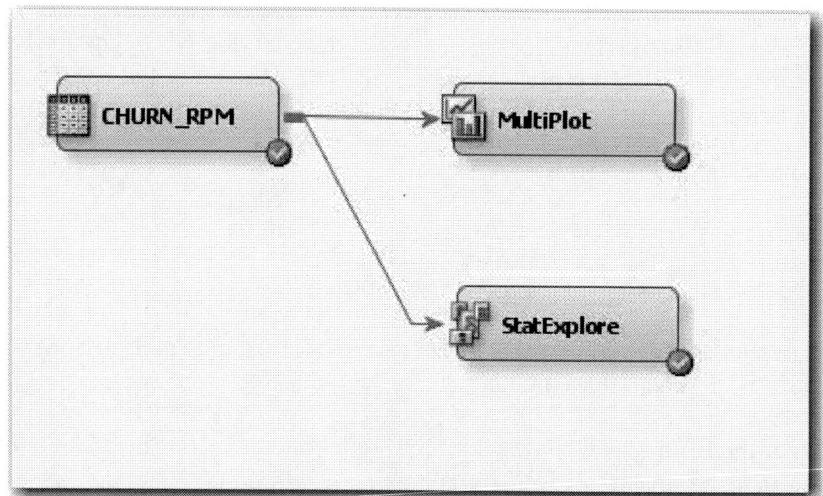

5. Select the **StatExplore** node in the workspace and examine the properties in the Properties panel.

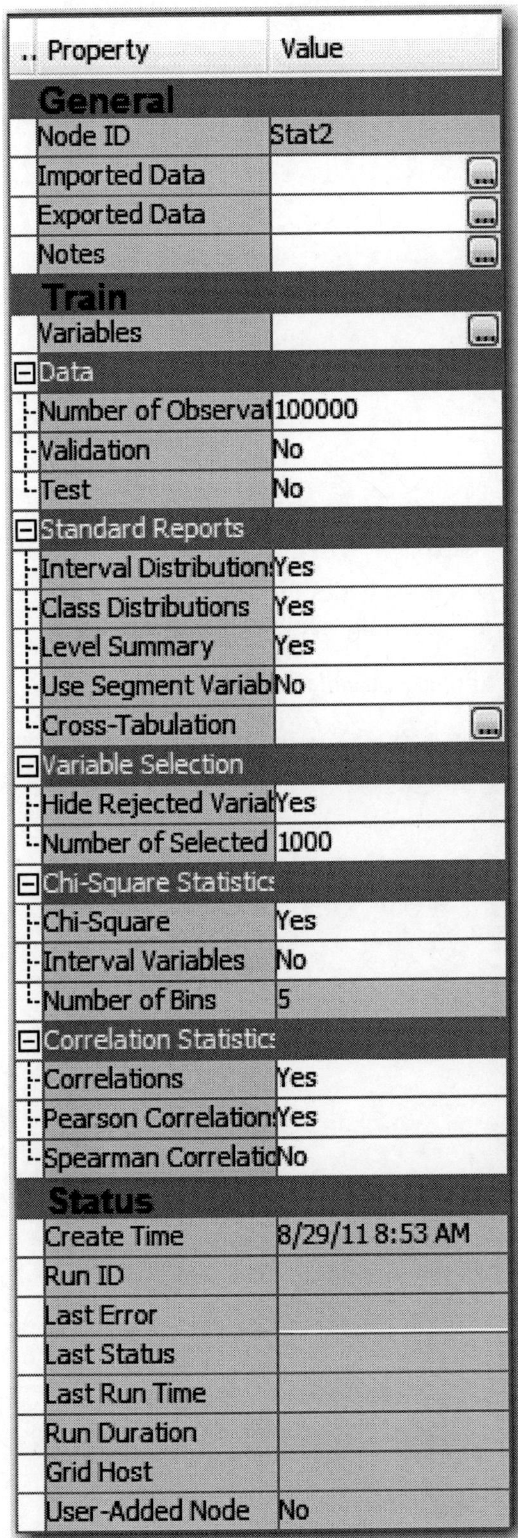


6. Right-click on the **StatExplore** node and select **Run**.

7. Select **Yes** when prompted to confirm that you want to run the path.

8. When the run is complete select **Results...**.

9. Examine the results in the Output window.

Data Role=TRAIN

| Variable | Role | Mean | Standard Deviation | Non Missing | Missing | Minimum | Median | Maximum | Skewness | Kurtosis |
|---|---|---|---|---|---|---|---|---|---|---|
| Account_Age | INPUT | 26.07965 | 7.149933 | 4708 | 0 | 15 | 25 | 40 | 0.287378 | -1.07702 |
| Avg_Calls | INPUT | 9269.69 | 10437.34 | 4708 | 0 | 0 | 6395.333 | 181786 | 3.426086 | 25.5527 |
| Avg_Calls_Weekdays | INPUT | 38127.99 | 39172.24 | 4708 | 0 | 0 | 26762 | 374457.7 | 2.473179 | 9.044002 |
| Avg_Days_Delinquent | INPUT | 13.96264 | 10.7879 | 4708 | 0 | 0 | 12.4 | 126 | 1.493373 | 5.328366 |
| Avg_Hours_WorkOrderOpenned | INPUT | 0.936501 | 8.926752 | 4708 | 0 | 0 | 0 | 297.5 | 19.0989 | 513.7663 |
| Current_Days_OpenWorkOrders | INPUT | 2.808305 | 22.17935 | 4708 | 0 | 0 | 0 | 368 | 10.57945 | 124.1086 |
| Equipment_Age | INPUT | 10.82434 | 8.7036 | 4708 | 0 | 0 | 9 | 39 | 0.781423 | 0.169213 |
| Percent_Increase_MOM | INPUT | -0.00513 | 4.481852 | 4708 | 0 | -1 | -0.18532 | 210.1 | 41.42824 | 1865.182 |
| current_billamount | INPUT | 19828.82 | 17204.51 | 4708 | 0 | -690 | 15254 | 325127 | 5.378004 | 56.41466 |

The output above is for interval variables and presents sample statistics for these variables. Information is also presented for class variables which includes information about the modes

In addition, you can see the same information for each of these variables by level of the target variable, **Churn_RPM**.

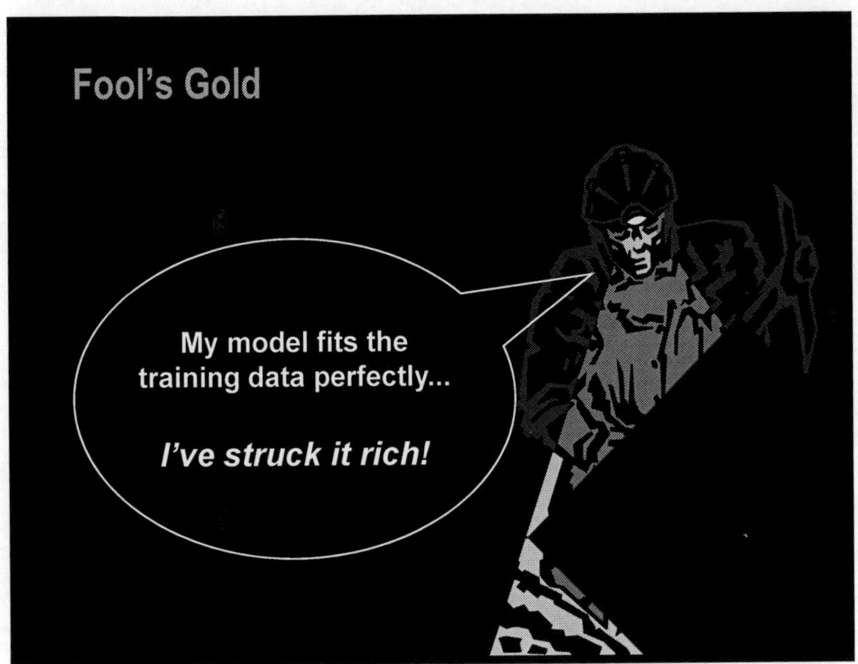


*Testing the procedure on the data that gave it birth is almost certain to overestimate performance, for the optimizing process that chose it from among many possible procedures will have made the greatest use of any and all idiosyncrasies of those particular data.*

— Mosteller and Tukey (1977)

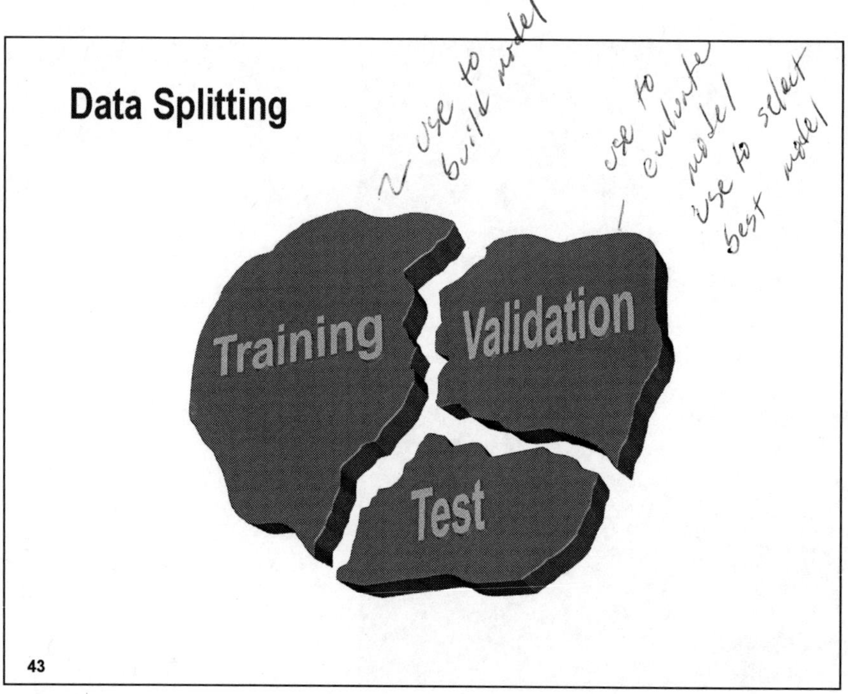


In data mining, the standard strategy for honest assessment of generalization is *data splitting*. **A portion is used for fitting the model: the training data set.** The rest is held out for empirical validation.

The *validation data set* is used for monitoring and tuning the model to improve its generalization. The tuning process usually involves selecting among models of different types and complexities. The tuning process optimizes the selected model on the validation data. Consequently, a further holdout sample is needed for a final, unbiased assessment.

The *test data set* has only one use: to give a final honest estimate of generalization. Consequently, cases in the test set must be treated just as new data would be treated. They cannot be involved whatsoever in the determination of the fitted prediction model. In some applications, there might be no need for a final honest assessment of generalization. A model can be optimized for performance on the test set by tuning it on the validation set. It might be enough to know that the prediction model will likely give the best generalization possible without actually being able to say what it is. In this situation, no test set is needed.

With small or moderate data sets, data splitting is inefficient; the reduced sample size can severely degrade the fit of the model. Computer-intensive methods such as cross-validation and the bootstrap have been developed so that all the data can be used for both fitting and honest assessment. However, data mining usually has the luxury of massive data sets.

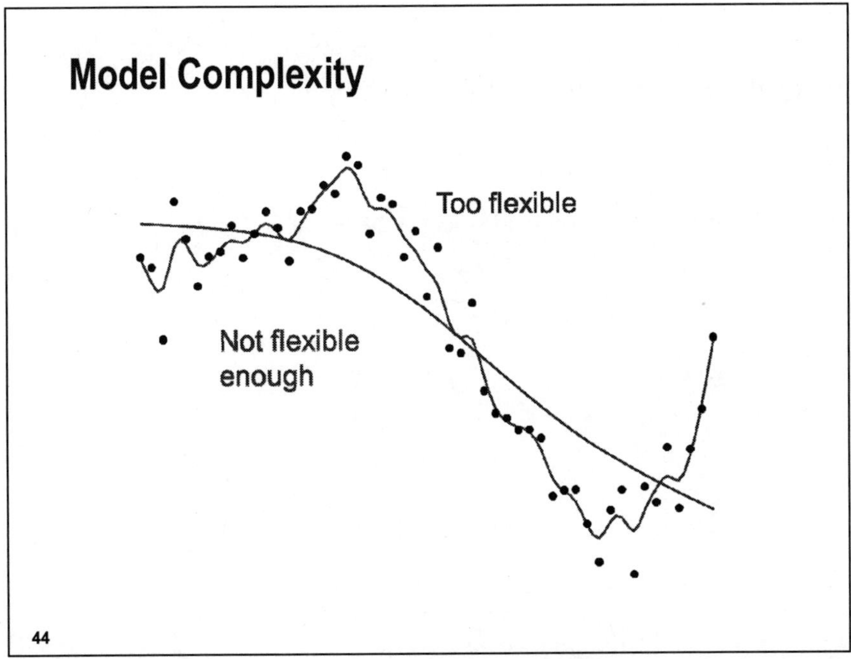


Fitting a model to data requires searching through the space of possible models. Constructing a model with good generalization requires choosing the right complexity.

Selecting model complexity involves a trade-off between bias and variance. An insufficiently complex model might not be flexible enough. This leads to underfitting – in other words, systematically missing the signal (high bias).

A naïve modeler might assume that the most complex model should always outperform the others, but this is not the case. An overly complex model might be too flexible. This will lead to overfitting – in other words, accommodating nuances of the random noise in the particular sample (high variance). A model with just enough flexibility will give the best generalization.

The strategy for choosing model complexity in data mining is to select the model that performs best on the validation data set. Using performance on the training data set usually leads to selecting a model that is too complex. (The classic example of this is selecting linear regression models based on R square.)

## Exploring the Data Partition Node

1. Right-click in an empty part of the diagram workspace and select **Add Node** ⇨ **Sample** ⇨ **Data Partition**.
2. Connect the Data Partition node to the **Churn_RPM** node.

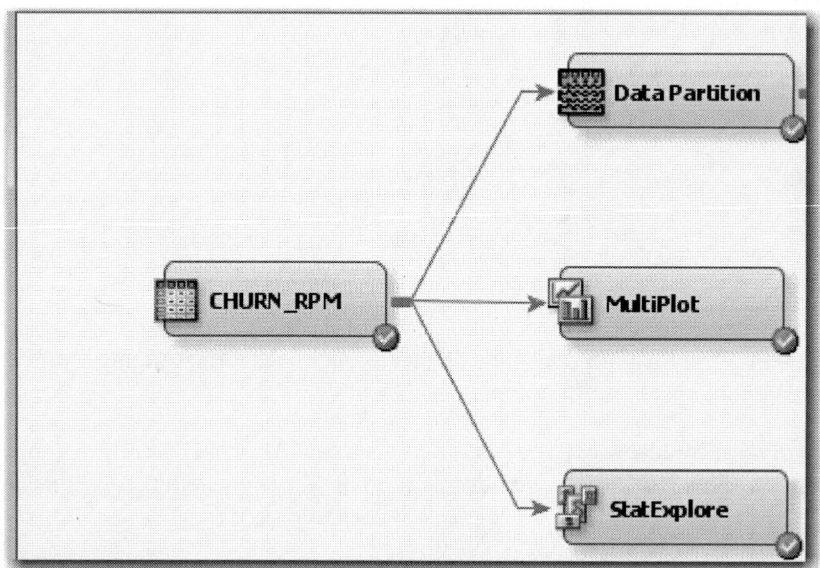


3. Select the **Data Partition** node in the workspace and examine the Properties panel.

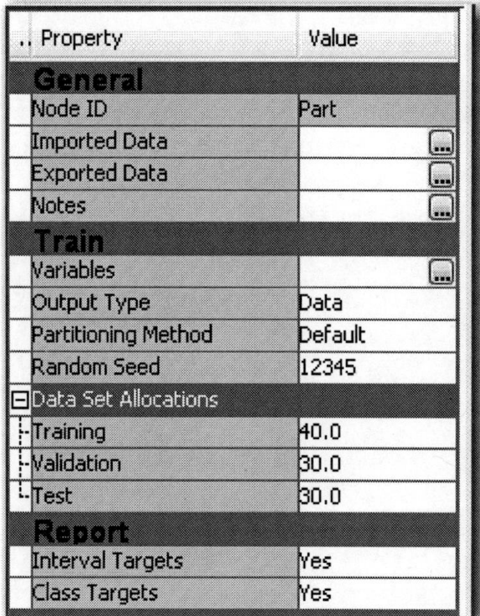

| Property | Value |
|---|---|
| **General** | |
| Node ID | Part |
| Imported Data | ... |
| Exported Data | ... |
| Notes | ... |
| **Train** | |
| Variables | ... |
| Output Type | Data |
| Partitioning Method | Default |
| Random Seed | 12345 |
| Data Set Allocations | |
| Training | 40.0 |
| Validation | 30.0 |
| Test | 30.0 |
| **Report** | |
| Interval Targets | Yes |
| Class Targets | Yes |

You choose the method for partitioning in the Train section of the panel. By default, if the target variable is a class variable, SAS Enterprise Miner takes a stratified random sample to divide the input data table into training, validation, and test data sets. The sampling is stratified on the target variable. If the target variable is not a class variable, then a simple random sample of the input data is used.

These are other sampling methods that can be chosen:

- Simple Random – use simple random sampling regardless of the nature of the target variable.
- Cluster – use simple cluster sampling to select a simple random sample of clusters (from a group of clusters) for each of the data sets specified (training, validation, and/or test). For example, if there are multiple records per customer, you might want to take a random sample of customers and then include all records of the selected customers in the sample.
- Stratified – use stratified sampling by specifying variables from the input data set to form strata (or subsets) of the total population. Within each stratum, a simple random sample is chosen.

In this section of the panel, you can also specify a random seed for initializing the sampling process. Randomization within computer programs is often started by some type of seed. If you use the same data set with the same seed in different flows, you get the same partition. Observe that re-sorting the data will result in a different ordering of data and, therefore, a different partition, which will potentially yield different results.

The center part of the **Properties** panel enables you to specify the percentage of the data to allocate to training, validation, and test data.

Partition the **Churn_RPM** data for modeling. Based on the data available, create training and validation data sets and omit the test data.

4. Set Training, Validation, and Test to **70**, **30**, and **0**, respectively.

| Data Set Allocations | |
|---|---|
| Training | 70.0 |
| Validation | 30.0 |
| Test | 0.0 |

The percentage values that you configure for Training, Validation, and Test must add up to 100%. If they do not, then the software will use the default percentage values.

5. To run the diagram from the Data Partition node, right-click on the node and select **Run**.
6. Select Yes to confirm that you want to run the path.
7. Select OK to acknowledge the completion of the run.

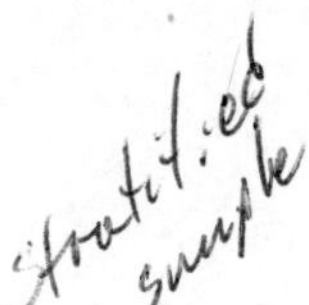

# 1.3 Introduction to Decision Trees

## Objectives

- Explore the general concept of decision trees.
- Build a decision tree model.
- Examine the model results and interpret these results.

47

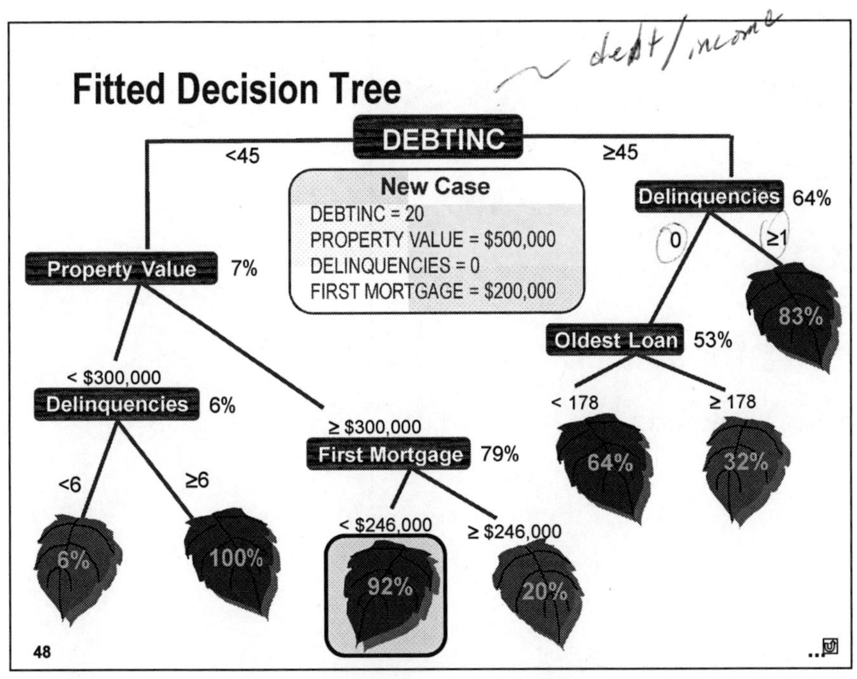


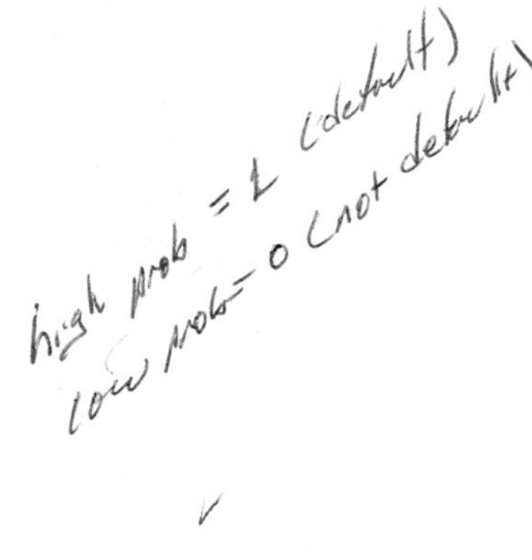


Interpretation of the fitted decision tree is straightforward. The *internal nodes* contain rules that involve one of the input variables. Start at the *root node* (top) and follow the rules until a terminal node (*leaf*) is reached. The leaves contain the estimate of the expected value of the target – in this case, the posterior probability of a default. The probability can then be used to allocate cases to classes. In this case, red denotes default and green denotes otherwise.

When the target is categorical, the decision tree is called a *classification tree*. When the target is continuous, it is called a *regression tree*.

The tree is fitted to the data by *recursive partitioning*. Partitioning refers to segmenting the data into subgroups that are as homogeneous as possible with respect to the target. In this case, the binary split (Debt-to-Income Ratio < 45) was chosen. The cases were split into two groups, one with a 64% default rate and the other with a 7% default rate.

The method is recursive because each subgroup results from splitting a subgroup from a previous split. Thus, the 3,224 cases in the left child node and the 946 cases in the right child node are split again in similar fashion.

## The Cultivation of Trees

- Split Search
  - Which splits are to be considered?
- Splitting Criterion
  - Which split is best?
- Stopping Rule
  - When should the splitting stop?
- Pruning Rule
  - Should some branches be lopped off?

49

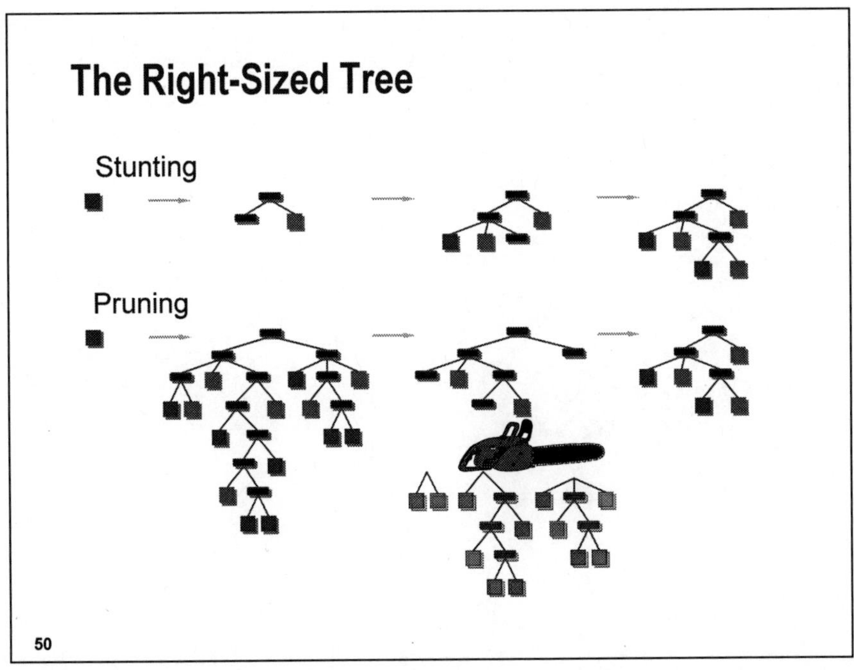


For decision trees, model complexity is measured by the number of leaves. A tree can be continually split until all leaves are pure or contain only one case. This tree would give a perfect fit to the training data but would probably give poor predictions on new data. At the other extreme, the tree could have only one leaf (the root node). Every case would have the same predicted value (no-data rule). There are two approaches to determining the right-sized tree:

1. Using forward-stopping rules to stunt the growth of a tree (*prepruning*).

   A universally accepted prepruning rule is to stop growing if the node is pure. Two other popular rules are to stop if the number of cases in a node falls below a specified limit or to stop when the split is not statistically significant at a specified level.

2. Growing a large tree and pruning back branches (*postpruning*).

   Postpruning creates a sequence of trees of increasing complexity. An assessment criterion is needed for deciding the best (sub) tree. The assessment criteria are usually based on performance on holdout samples (validation data or with cross-validation). Cost or profit considerations can be incorporated into the assessment.

   Prepruning is less computationally demanding but runs the risk of missing future splits that occur below weak splits.

## Benefits of Trees

- Interpretability
  - tree-structured presentation
- Mixed Measurement Scales
  - nominal, ordinal, interval
- Regression trees
- Robustness
- Missing Values

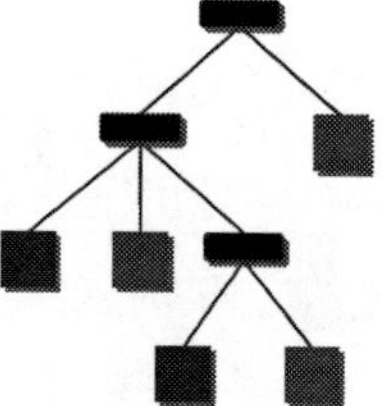

51

The tree diagram is useful for assessing which variables are important and how they interact with each other. The results can often be written as simple rules such as the following:

> If (**DEBTINC** ≥ 45 and **Delinquencies** ≥ 1) or
> (**DEBTINC** ≥ 45 and **Delinquencies** = 0 and **CLAGE** < 178),
> then **Default** = yes; otherwise, no.

Splits based on numeric input variables depend only on the rank order of the values. Like many nonparametric methods based on ranks, trees are robust to outliers in the input space.

Recursive partitioning has special ways of treating missing values. One approach is to treat missing values as a separate level of the input variable. The missing values could be grouped with other values in a node or have their own node. Another approach is to use surrogate splits; if a particular case has a missing value for the chosen split, you can use a nonmissing input variable that gives a similar split instead.

## Benefits of Trees

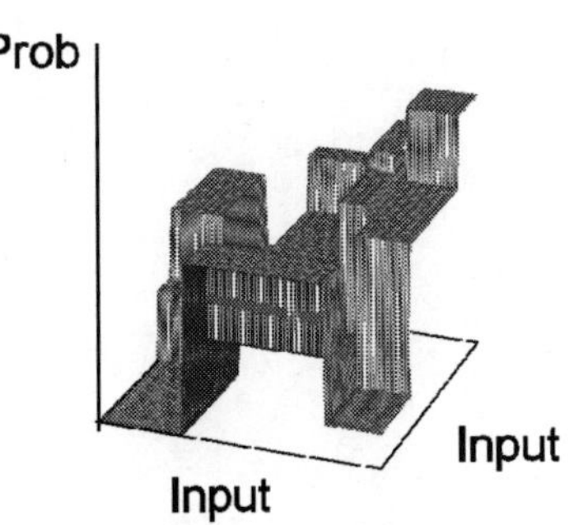


**Multivariate Step Function**

- Automatically does the following:
  - detects interactions (AID)
  - accommodates nonlinearity
  - selects input variables

52

## Drawbacks of Trees

- Roughness
- Linear, Main Effects
- Instability

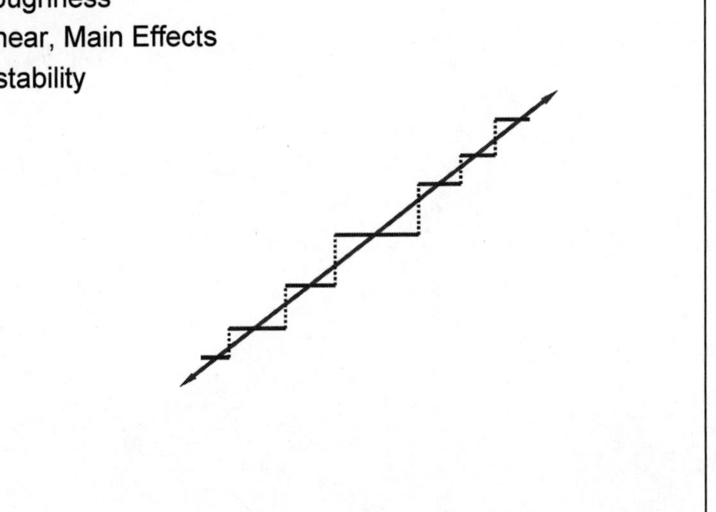

53

The fitted model is composed of discontinuous flat surfaces. The predicted values do not vary smoothly across the input space like other models. This roughness is the trade-off for interpretability.

A step function fitted to a straight line needs many small steps. When input variables do not interact with each other, the structure of the model can be more complex than is necessary. Consequently, linear additive inputs can produce complicated trees that miss the simple structure.

Trees are unstable because small perturbations in the training data can sometimes have large effects on the internal structure of the tree. The effect of altering a split is compounded as it cascades down the tree and as the sample size decreases.

## Building and Interpreting Decision Trees

1. To complete the first phase of your first diagram, add a **Decision Tree** node to the workspace and connect it to the **Data Partition** node.

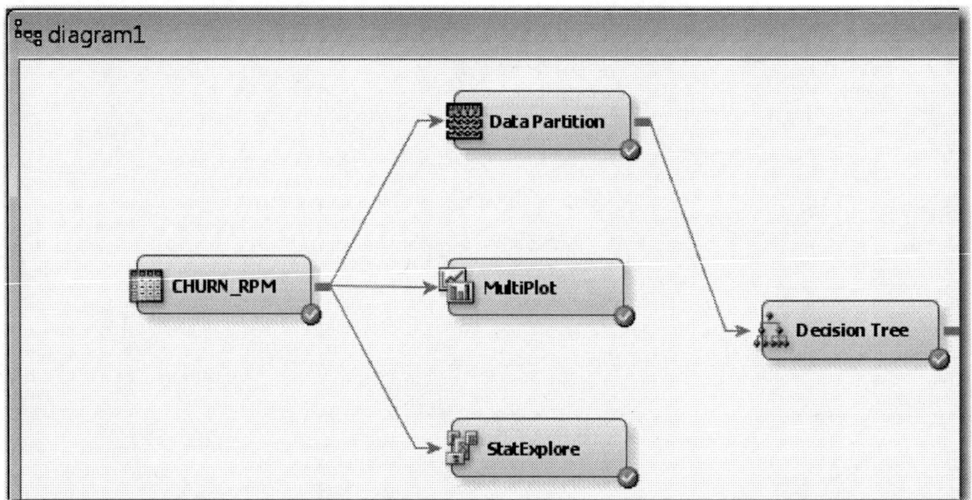

Examine the default setting for the decision tree.

2. Select the **Decision Tree** node and examine the Properties panel.

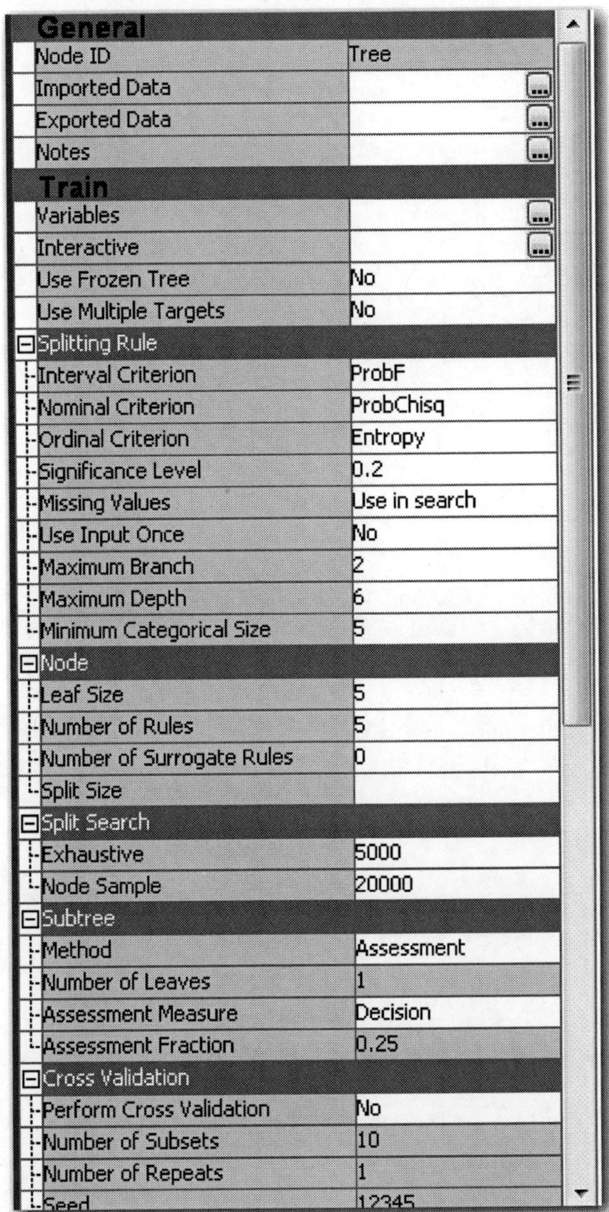

General
Node ID Tree
Imported Data
Exported Data
Notes
Train
Variables
Interactive
Use Frozen Tree No
Use Multiple Targets No
Splitting Rule
Interval Criterion ProbF
Nominal Criterion ProbChisq
Ordinal Criterion Entropy
Significance Level 0.2
Missing Values Use in search
Use Input Once No
Maximum Branch 2
Maximum Depth 6
Minimum Categorical Size 5
Node
Leaf Size 5
Number of Rules 5
Number of Surrogate Rules 0
Split Size
Split Search
Exhaustive 5000
Node Sample 20000
Subtree
Method Assessment
Number of Leaves 1
Assessment Measure Decision
Assessment Fraction 0.25
Cross Validation
Perform Cross Validation No
Number of Subsets 10
Number of Repeats 1
Seed 12345


Change the assessment measure to **Average Square Error** from **Decision**. Thus **Average Square Error** on the validation dataset will be used to select the model.

3. Select the ... button in the **Variables** row to examine the variables to ensure that all variables have the appropriate status, role, and level.

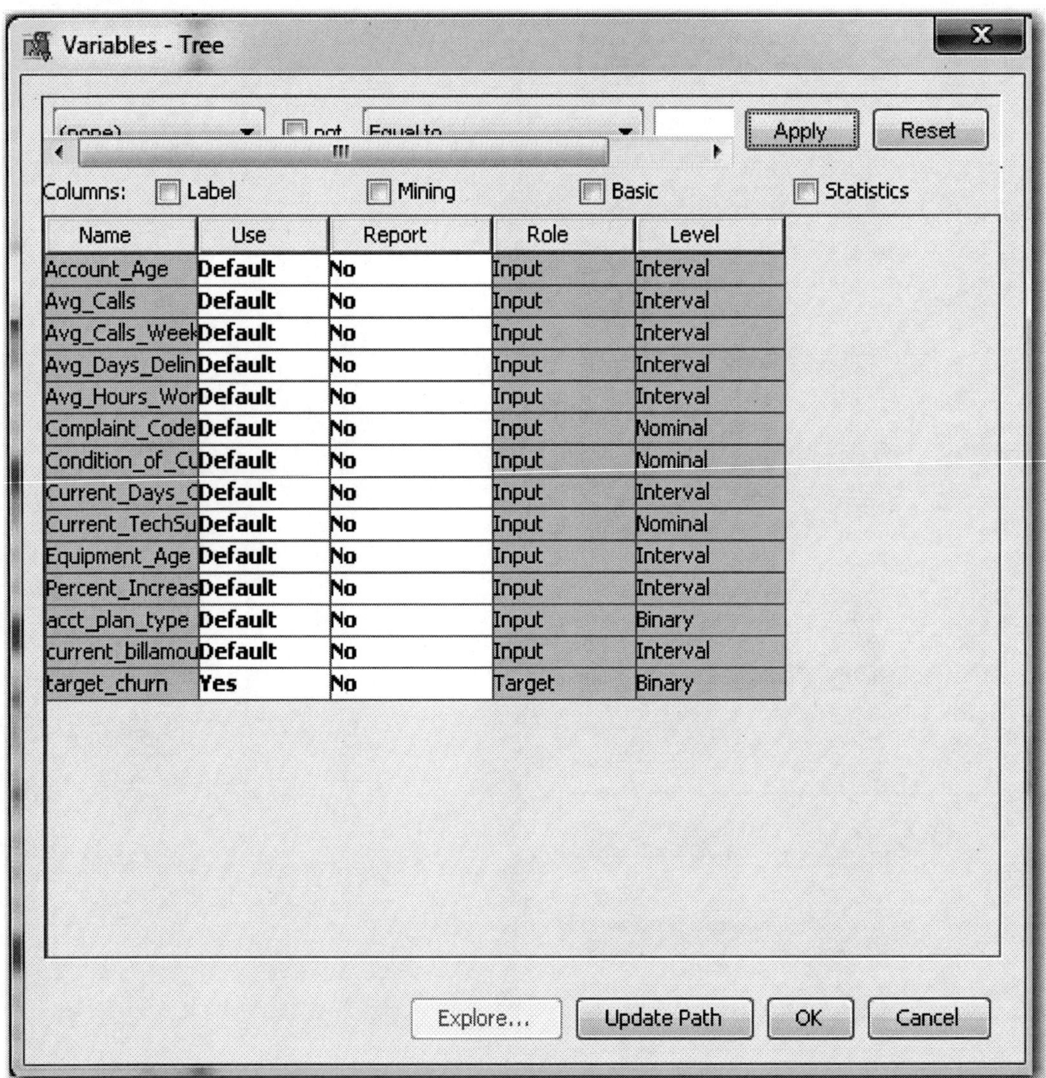


If the role or level were not correct, it could not be corrected in this node. You would return to the Input Data node to make the corrections.

4. Select **OK** to close the Variables window and continue to examine the Properties panel.

   Many of the options discussed earlier for building a decision tree are controlled in the Properties panel.

   The splitting criteria that are available depend on the measurement level of the target variable. For binary or nominal target variables, the default splitting criterion is the chi-square test. For ordinal target variables, entropy is the default splitting criterion, and for interval targets the default splitting criterion is the *F* test. Other available methods include Gini reduction and variance reduction.

   The significance level property is used to specify the threshold *p*-value for the worth of a candidate splitting rule. For the chi-square and *F*-test criteria, the threshold is the maximum acceptable *p*-value. For other criteria, the threshold is the minimum acceptable increase in the measure of worth.

The missing value property determines how splitting rules handle observations that contain a missing value for a variable. The options available include the following:

- Use in search – uses the missing values during the split search. This is the default.
- Most correlated branch – assigns the observation with the missing value to the branch that minimizes the Sum of Squared Error among observations that contain missing values.
- Largest branch – assigns the observations that contain missing values to the largest branch.

The other options that are available in the Properties panel affect the growth and size of the tree. By default, only binary splits are permitted, the maximum depth of the tree is six levels, and the minimum number of observations in a leaf is five.

The following are other properties that are shown in the Properties panel that affect the growth of the tree:

- The minimum categorical size property specifies the minimum number of observations a category variable level must have before the level can be used in a split search.
- The number of rules property specifies the number of splitting rules that will be saved with each node.
- The number of surrogate rules property specifies the maximum number of surrogate rules that the decision tree will seek in each non-leaf node.
- The split size property specifies the required number of observations in a node in order to split the node. The default is two times the leaf size

> There are additional options available in the Properties panel. All of the options are discussed in greater detail in the Decision Tree Modeling course.

5. Right-click on the **Decision Tree** node and select **Run**.
6. When prompted, select Yes to run the diagram.
7. When the run is completed, select Results... .

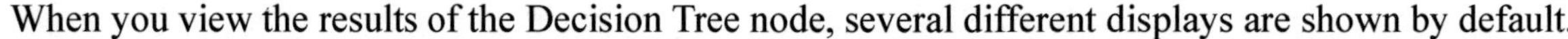

When you view the results of the Decision Tree node, several different displays are shown by default.

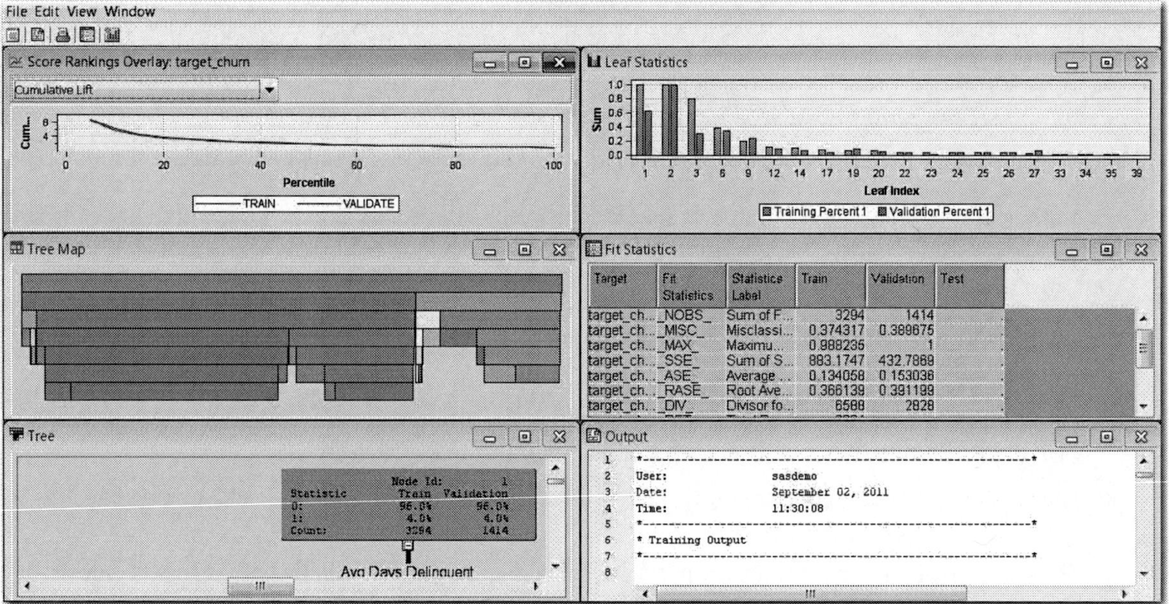


8. Maximize the Tree Map window to examine it more closely.

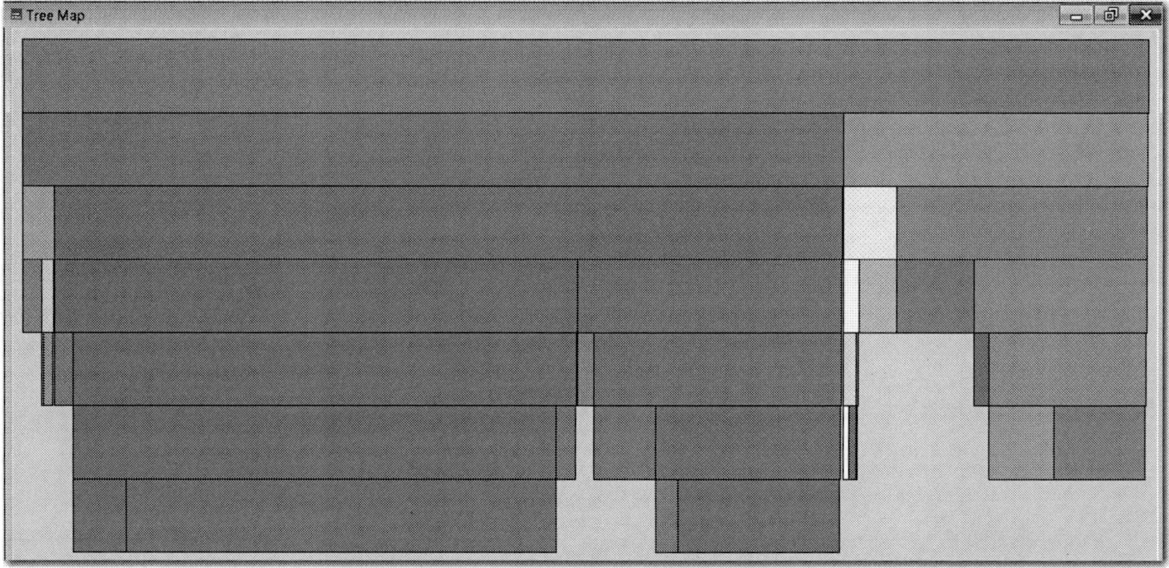


The tree map shows the way that the tree was split. The final tree appears to have 6 leaves, but it is difficult to be sure because some leaves can be so small that they are almost invisible on the map. You can use your cursor to display information on each of the leaves as well as the intermediate nodes of the tree.

9. Maximize the Output window.

```
Variable Summary

          Measurement    Frequency
 Role        Level         Count

INPUT      BINARY            1
INPUT      INTERVAL          9
INPUT      NOMINAL           3
TARGET     BINARY            1
```

10. Scroll down the Output window to view the Variable Importance table.

Variable Importance

| Obs | NAME | LABEL | NRULES | IMPORTANCE | VIMPORTANCE | RATIO |
|---|---|---|---|---|---|---|
| 1 | Avg_Days_Delinquent | Avg Days Delinquent | 3 | 1.00000 | 1.00000 | 1.00000 |
| 2 | Percent_Increase_MOM | Percent_Increase_MOM | 6 | 0.73778 | 0.78149 | 1.05925 |
| 3 | Complaint_Code | | 3 | 0.28096 | 0.30822 | 1.09704 |
| 4 | Avg_Calls_Weekdays | Avg Calls Weekdays | 3 | 0.21770 | 0.03854 | 0.17705 |
| 5 | current_billamount | Current Bill Amt | 1 | 0.14296 | 0.08194 | 0.57314 |
| 6 | acct_plan_type | Acct Plan Subtype | 2 | 0.09197 | 0.05688 | 0.61839 |
| 7 | Avg_Hours_WorkOrderOpenned | Avg Hours WorkOrderOpenned | 1 | 0.04855 | 0.04240 | 0.87322 |

The table shows the variable name and label, the number of rules (or splits) in the tree that involve the variable (**NRULES**), the importance of the variable computed with the training data (**IMPORTANCE**), the importance of the variable computed with the validation data (**VIMPORTANCE**), and the ratio of **VIMPORTANCE** to **IMPORTANCE**. The calculation of importance is a function of the number of splits the variable is used in, the number of observations at each of those splits, and the relative purity of each of the splits.

11. Scroll down further in the output to examine the Tree Leaf Report.

Tree Leaf Report

| Node | Depth | Training Observations | Training Percent 1 | Validation Observations | Validation Percent 1 |
|---|---|---|---|---|---|
| 47 | 6 | 1268.03 | 0.00 | 511.798 | 0.00 |
| 49 | 6 | 470.55 | 0.01 | 188.694 | 0.01 |
| 45 | 5 | 268.95 | 0.06 | 109.831 | 0.05 |
| 14 | 3 | 224.50 | 0.03 | 75.208 | 0.03 |
| 44 | 5 | 194.08 | 0.12 | 116.473 | 0.09 |
| 38 | 5 | 182.53 | 0.03 | 65.789 | 0.04 |
| 46 | 6 | 157.88 | 0.01 | 93.935 | 0.01 |
| 13 | 3 | 108.65 | 0.19 | 41.786 | 0.24 |
| 48 | 6 | 67.72 | 0.04 | 26.881 | 0.03 |
| 37 | 5 | 59.10 | 0.02 | 15.843 | 0.06 |
| 20 | 4 | 55.95 | 0.03 | 28.255 | 0.01 |
| 8 | 3 | 55.64 | 0.06 | 18.451 | 0.09 |
| 22 | 4 | 50.04 | 0.07 | 27.128 | 0.04 |
| 30 | 4 | 45.21 | 0.01 | 35.888 | 0.01 |
| 19 | 4 | 29.02 | 0.10 | 21.856 | 0.06 |
| 41 | 5 | 22.65 | 1.00 | 14.740 | 0.62 |
| 40 | 5 | 18.20 | 0.38 | 11.338 | 0.34 |
| 18 | 4 | 8.78 | 0.79 | 7.989 | 0.30 |
| 42 | 5 | 5.76 | 0.03 | 1.950 | 0.04 |
| 43 | 5 | 0.74 | 1.00 | 0.165 | 1.00 |

This report shows that the tree does have 6 leaves as it appeared to have from looking at the tree map. The leaves in the table are in order from the largest number of training observations to the fewest training observations. Notice that details are given for both the training and validation data sets.

12. Maximize the Tree window to examine the decision tree itself.

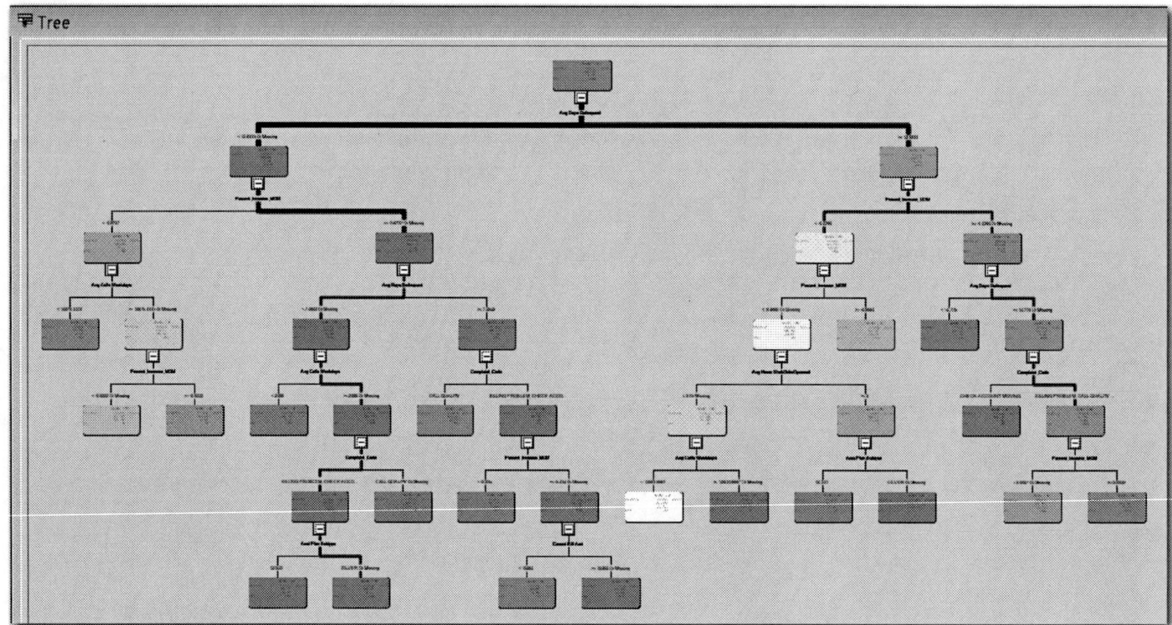


The default decision tree has the following properties:

- It is displayed in vertical orientation.
- The line width is proportional to the ratio of the number of observations in the branch to the number of observations in the root, or top, node.
- The line color is constant.

All of these default properties can be changed.

In this case, you can see that the first split was based on the avg days delinquent, but you cannot see much of the tree because of its size.

13. The English Rules window provides a written description of the leaves of the tree. To open the English Rules window, select **View ⇨ Model ⇨ English Rules**.

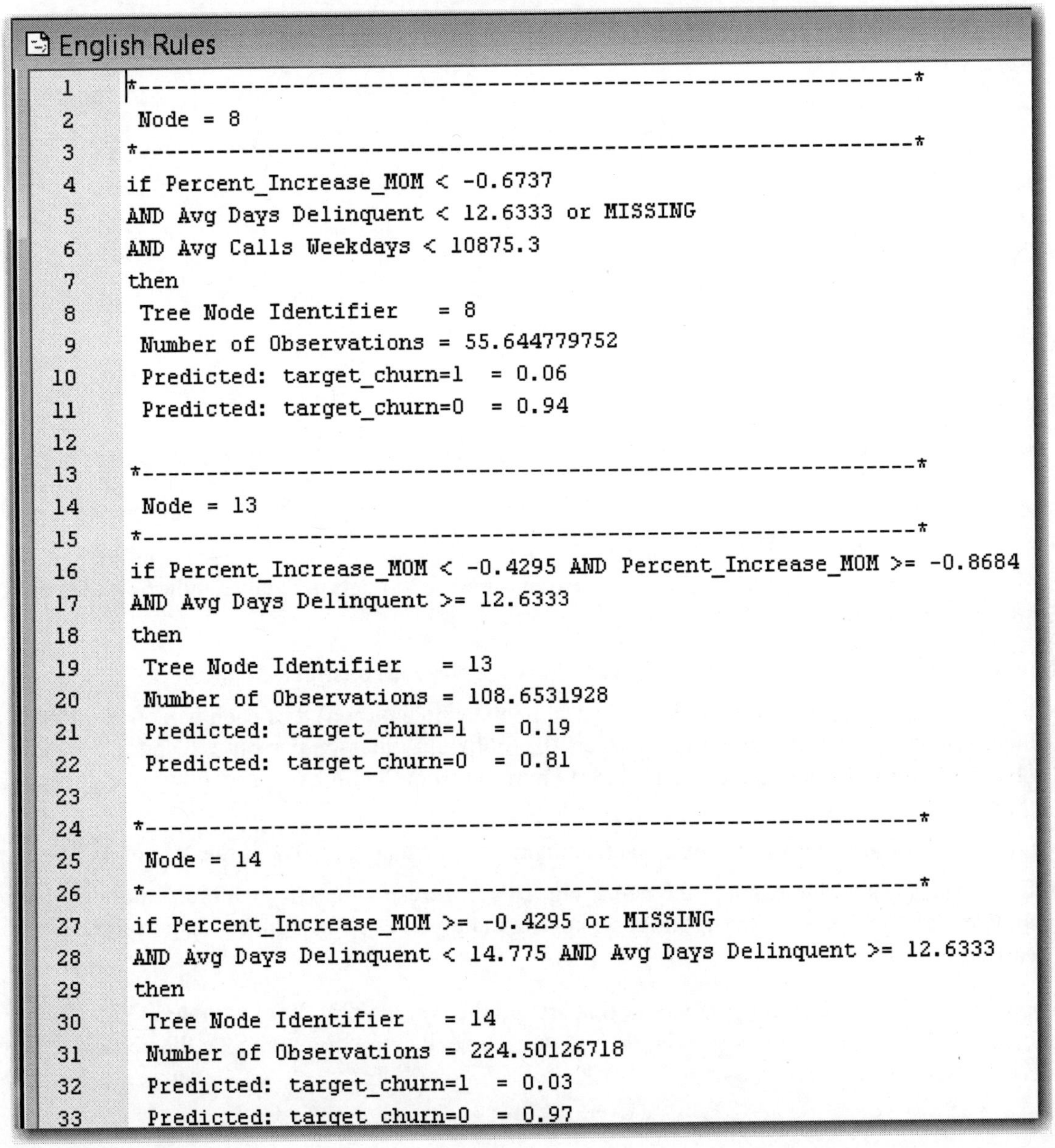

English Rules

```
*------------------------------------------------------------*
 Node = 8
*------------------------------------------------------------*
if Percent_Increase_MOM < -0.6737
AND Avg Days Delinquent < 12.6333 or MISSING
AND Avg Calls Weekdays < 10875.3
then
 Tree Node Identifier   = 8
 Number of Observations = 55.644779752
 Predicted: target_churn=1  = 0.06
 Predicted: target_churn=0  = 0.94

*------------------------------------------------------------*
 Node = 13
*------------------------------------------------------------*
if Percent_Increase_MOM < -0.4295 AND Percent_Increase_MOM >= -0.8684
AND Avg Days Delinquent >= 12.6333
then
 Tree Node Identifier   = 13
 Number of Observations = 108.6531928
 Predicted: target_churn=1  = 0.19
 Predicted: target_churn=0  = 0.81

*------------------------------------------------------------*
 Node = 14
*------------------------------------------------------------*
if Percent_Increase_MOM >= -0.4295 or MISSING
AND Avg Days Delinquent < 14.775 AND Avg Days Delinquent >= 12.6333
then
 Tree Node Identifier   = 14
 Number of Observations = 224.50126718
 Predicted: target_churn=1  = 0.03
 Predicted: target_churn=0  = 0.97
```

14. Close the English Rules window and maximize the Score Rankings Overlay chart.

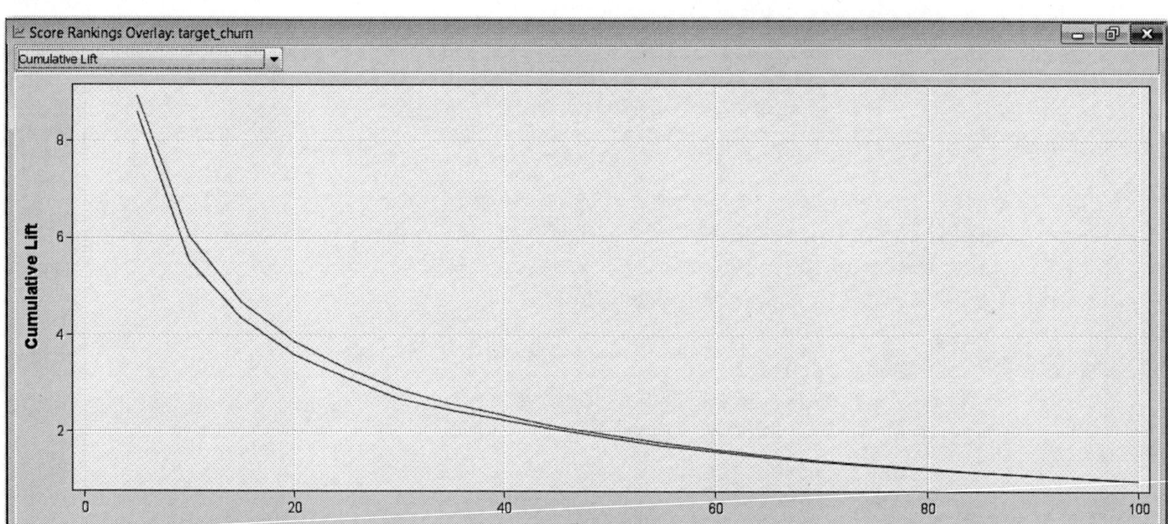


A cumulative lift chart is shown by default. To see actual values, place the cursor over the plot at any decile. For example, placing the cursor over the plot for the validation data set indicates a lift of 2.23 for the 40th percentile.

To interpret the cumulative lift chart, consider how the chart is constructed.

- For this example, a responder is defined as someone who churned). For each person, the fitted model (in this case, a decision tree) predicts the probability that the person will churn. Sort the observations by the predicted probability of churning from the highest probability of churning to the lowest probability of churning.
- Group the people into ordered bins, each containing approximately 5% of the data in this case.
- Using the target variable, count the percentage of actual responders in each bin and divide that by the population response rate (in this case, approximately 4%, as seen during data exploration earlier).

You have the option to change the values that are graphed on the plot. For example, if you are interested in the percent of people who default in each decile, you might change the vertical axis to percent response.

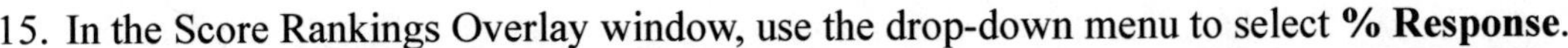

15. In the Score Rankings Overlay window, use the drop-down menu to select **% Response**.

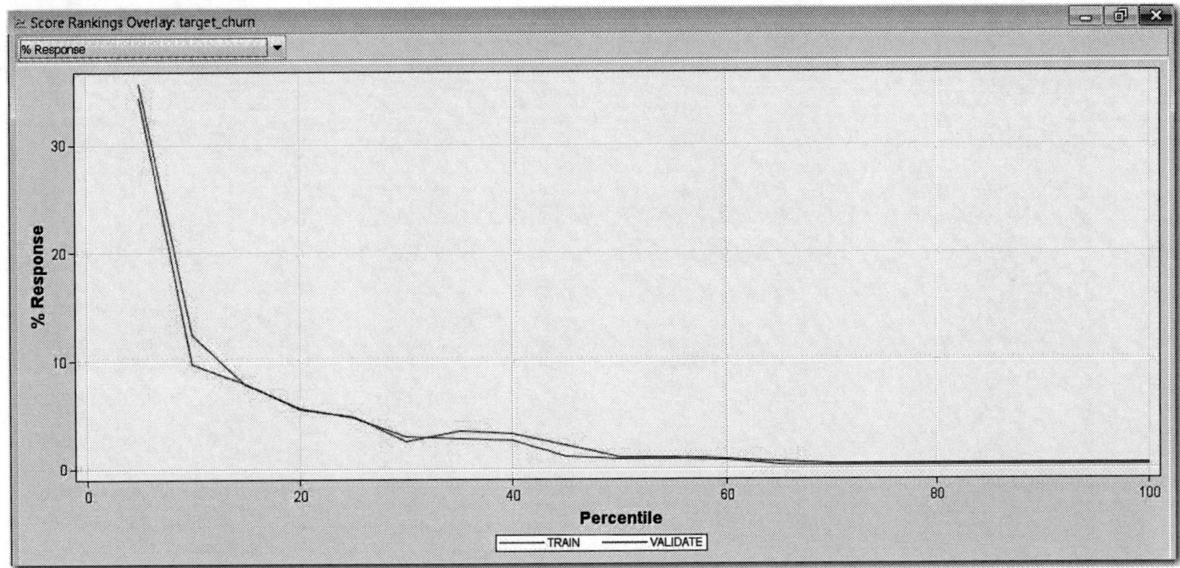


This non-cumulative percent response chart shows that after you get beyond the 30th percentile for predicted probability on the decision tree, the churn rate is lower than what you would expect if you were to take a random sample.

Instead of asking the question "What percentage of observations in a bin were defaulters?", you could ask the question "What percentage of the total number of churners are in a bin?" This can be evaluated using the cumulative percent captured response as the response variable in the graph.

16. In the Score Rankings Overlay window, use the drop-down menu to select **Cumulative % Captured Response**.

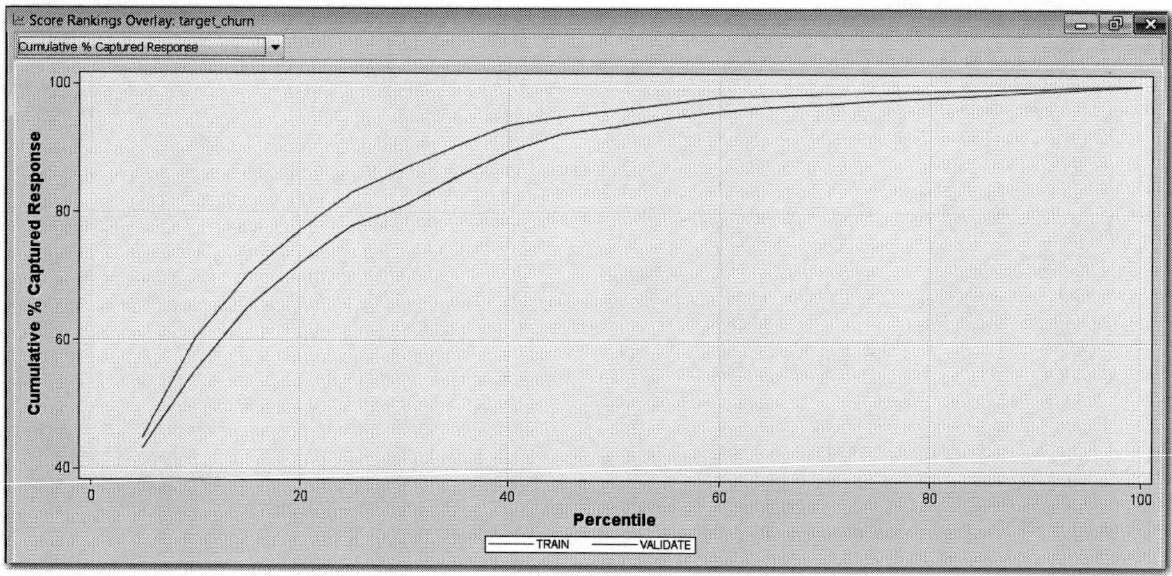


Observe that using the validation data set, if the percentage of customers selected for churning were approximately

- 20%, then you would have identified close to 70% of the people who would have churned.
- 30%, then you would have identified almost 81% of the people who would have churned.

After you are finished examining the tree results, close the results and return to the diagram.

## Using Tree Options

You can make adjustments to the default tree algorithm that causes your tree to grow differently. These changes do not necessarily improve the classification performance of the tree, but they might improve its interpretability.

The Decision Tree node splits a node into two nodes by default (called *binary splits*). In theory, trees that use multiway splits are no more flexible or powerful than trees that use binary splits. The primary goal is to increase interpretability of the final result. You can change the setting in the property panel to allow multiway splits. Various stopping or stunting rules (also known as *prepruning*) can be used to limit the growth of a decision tree. For example, it might be deemed beneficial not to split a node with fewer than 50 cases and require that each node have at least 25 cases. This can be done in SAS Enterprise Miner using the Leaf Size property in the Properties panel.

1. Select **View** ⇨ **Model** ⇨ **Subtree Assessment Plot** to examine the iteration plot shown below. The subtree that is selected is the smallest tree with the minimum misclassification rate on the validation data set. In this case, the smallest tree has 20 leaves and the validation misclassification rate is 0.153. A drop-down menu enables you to examine other assessment plots.

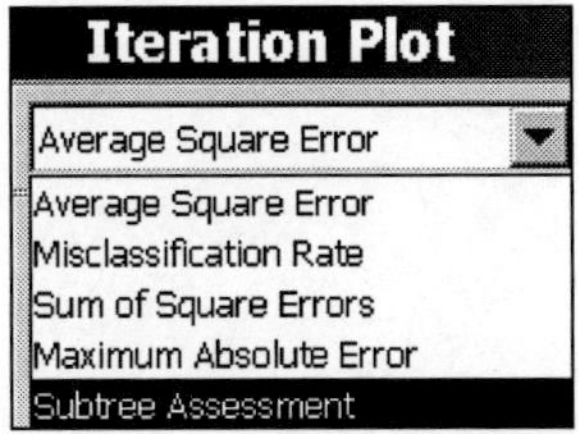


2. Select **Average Square Error** to produces the graphic shown below.

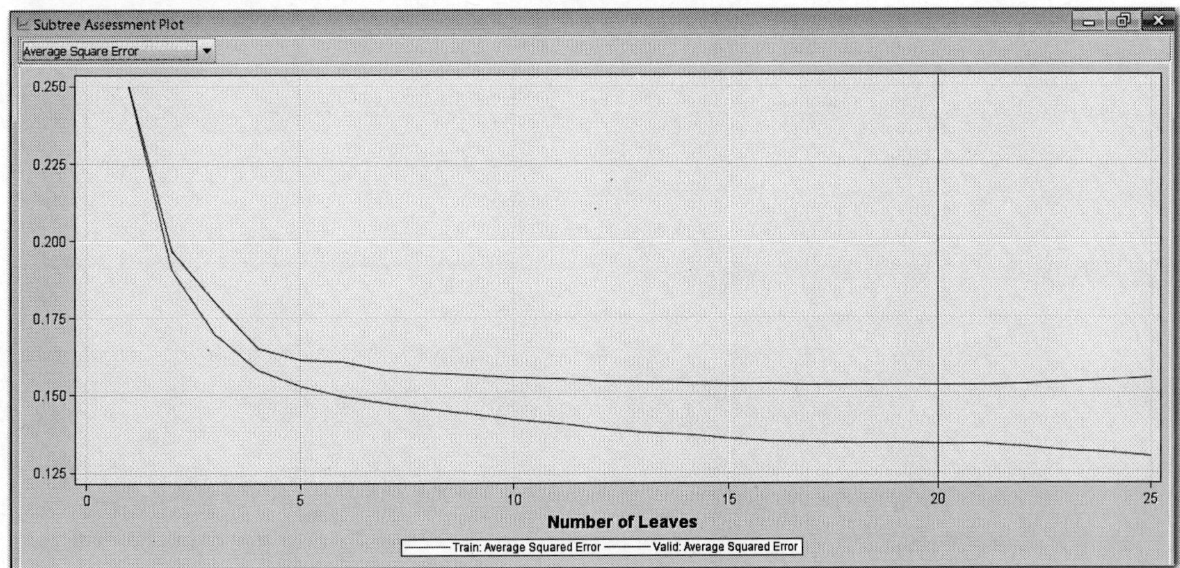

3. Select **View** ⇨ **Table** to examine the data that produces the plot.

Table: Subtree Assessment Plot

| Train: Subtree Assesame nt | Valid: Subtree Assessme nt | Train: Sum of Frequenci es | Train: Sum of Case Weights Times Freq | Number of Leaves | Train: Misclassifi cation Rate | Train: Maximum Absolute Error | Train: Sum of Squared Errors | Train: Average Squared Error | Train: Root Average Squared Error | Train: Divisor for ASE | Train: Total Degrees of Freedom | Train: Average Profit for target_chu rn | Train: Total Profit for target_chu rn | Train: Average Squared Error with Priors | Train: Misclassifi cation Rate with Priors | Valid: Sum o Freque es |
|---|---|---|---|---|---|---|---|---|---|---|---|---|---|---|---|---|
| 0.499593 | 0.4996 | 3294 | 6588 | 1 | 0.485732 | 0.514268 | 1645.659 | 0.249796 | 0.499796 | 6588 | 3294 | 1 | 3294 | 0.437055 | 0.04 | |
| 0.38072 | 0.39312 | 3294 | 6588 | 2 | 0.485732 | 0.751924 | 1254.093 | 0.19036 | 0.436303 | 6588 | 3294 | 1.48783 | 4900.811 | 0.398127 | 0.04 | |
| 0.339854 | 0.360672 | 3294 | 6588 | 3 | 0.485732 | 0.825707 | 1119.479 | 0.169927 | 0.412222 | 6588 | 3294 | 1.562446 | 5146.698 | 0.38905 | 0.04 | |
| 0.316079 | 0.330343 | 3294 | 6588 | 4 | 0.485732 | 0.917768 | 1041.164 | 0.158039 | 0.397542 | 6588 | 3294 | 1.562446 | 5146.698 | 0.340265 | 0.04 | |
| 0.305654 | 0.322857 | 3294 | 6588 | 5 | 0.485732 | 0.917768 | 1006.825 | 0.152827 | 0.390931 | 6588 | 3294 | 1.562446 | 5146.698 | 0.338464 | 0.04 | |
| 0.298941 | 0.322005 | 3294 | 6588 | 6 | 0.485732 | 0.917768 | 984.7112 | 0.14947 | 0.386614 | 6588 | 3294 | 1.585263 | 5221.858 | 0.336856 | 0.04 | |
| 0.294626 | 0.315966 | 3294 | 6588 | 7 | 0.485732 | 0.917768 | 970.4969 | 0.147313 | 0.383814 | 6588 | 3294 | 1.596306 | 5258.232 | 0.335336 | 0.04 | |
| 0.290803 | 0.314413 | 3294 | 6588 | 8 | 0.485732 | 0.917768 | 957.9055 | 0.145402 | 0.381316 | 6588 | 3294 | 1.596306 | 5258.232 | 0.332082 | 0.04 | |
| 0.287822 | 0.313064 | 3294 | 6588 | 9 | 0.485732 | 0.917768 | 948.0862 | 0.143911 | 0.379356 | 6588 | 3294 | 1.607173 | 5294.028 | 0.334242 | 0.04 | |
| 0.284 | 0.311511 | 3294 | 6588 | 10 | 0.485732 | 0.917768 | 935.4949 | 0.142 | 0.376829 | 6588 | 3294 | 1.607173 | 5294.028 | 0.330988 | 0.04 | |
| 0.281964 | 0.310639 | 3294 | 6588 | 11 | 0.485732 | 0.947761 | 928.7886 | 0.140982 | 0.375476 | 6588 | 3294 | 1.607173 | 5294.028 | 0.333791 | 0.04 | |
| 0.278141 | 0.309086 | 3294 | 6588 | 12 | 0.485732 | 0.947761 | 916.1973 | 0.139071 | 0.372922 | 6588 | 3294 | 1.607173 | 5294.028 | 0.330536 | 0.04 | |
| 0.275361 | 0.308315 | 3294 | 6588 | 13 | 0.485732 | 0.947761 | 907.0406 | 0.137681 | 0.371054 | 6588 | 3294 | 1.607173 | 5294.028 | 0.33024 | 0.04 | |
| 0.274337 | 0.30784 | 3294 | 6588 | 14 | 0.460534 | 0.988235 | 903.6659 | 0.137168 | 0.370363 | 6588 | 3294 | 1.607173 | 5294.028 | 0.315834 | 0.038467 | |
| 0.271557 | 0.307069 | 3294 | 6588 | 15 | 0.460534 | 0.988235 | 894.5092 | 0.135779 | 0.368481 | 6588 | 3294 | 1.607173 | 5294.028 | 0.315538 | 0.038467 | |
| 0.269768 | 0.306821 | 3294 | 6588 | 16 | 0.350638 | 0.988235 | 888.6151 | 0.134884 | 0.367265 | 6588 | 3294 | 1.607173 | 5294.028 | 0.295148 | 0.034292 | |
| 0.269447 | 0.306615 | 3294 | 6588 | 17 | 0.353066 | 0.988235 | 887.559 | 0.134724 | 0.367047 | 6588 | 3294 | 1.607173 | 5294.028 | 0.291595 | 0.032867 | |
| 0.268745 | 0.306282 | 3294 | 6588 | 18 | 0.350334 | 0.988235 | 885.2447 | 0.134372 | 0.366568 | 6588 | 3294 | 1.607694 | 5295.744 | 0.289725 | 0.032642 | |
| 0.268564 | 0.306112 | 3294 | 6588 | 19 | 0.374317 | 0.988235 | 884.6502 | 0.134282 | 0.366445 | 6588 | 3294 | 1.607694 | 5295.744 | 0.290568 | 0.031367 | |
| 0.268116 | 0.306073 | 3294 | 6588 | 20 | 0.374317 | 0.988235 | 883.1747 | 0.134058 | 0.366139 | 6588 | 3294 | 1.607694 | 5295.744 | 0.290545 | 0.031367 | |
| 0.268002 | 0.30628 | 3294 | 6588 | 21 | 0.375228 | 0.958982 | 882.7982 | 0.134001 | 0.366061 | 6588 | 3294 | 1.607694 | 5295.744 | 0.290101 | 0.0309 | |
| 0.266262 | 0.306769 | 3294 | 6588 | 22 | 0.375228 | 0.958982 | 877.0673 | 0.133131 | 0.364871 | 6588 | 3294 | 1.609292 | 5301.007 | 0.287394 | 0.0309 | |
| 0.263991 | 0.307912 | 3294 | 6588 | 23 | 0.375228 | 0.958982 | 869.5857 | 0.131995 | 0.363312 | 6588 | 3294 | 1.614533 | 5318.271 | 0.287004 | 0.0309 | |
| 0.2625 | 0.30916 | 3294 | 6588 | 24 | 0.375228 | 0.958982 | 864.6759 | 0.13125 | 0.362285 | 6588 | 3294 | 1.614533 | 5318.271 | 0.285017 | 0.0309 | |
| 0.260143 | 0.311541 | 3294 | 6588 | 25 | 0.375228 | 0.958982 | 856.9096 | 0.130071 | 0.360654 | 6588 | 3294 | 1.621547 | 5341.375 | 0.284227 | 0.0309 | |

# 1.4 Introduction to Regression

## Objectives

- Describe linear and logistic regression.
- Explore data issues associated with regression.
- Discuss variable selection methods.
- Conduct missing value imputation.
- Examine transformations of data.
- Generate a regression model.
- Compare models.

56

## Linear versus Logistic Regression

| Linear Regression | Logistic Regression |
|---|---|
| Target is an interval variable. | Target is a discrete variable. |
| Input variables have any measurement level. | Input variables have any measurement level. |
| Predicted values are the mean of the target variable at the given values of the input variables. | Predicted values are the probability of a particular level(s) of the target variable at the given values of the input variables. |

57

The Regression node in SAS Enterprise Miner does either linear or logistic regression depending upon the measurement level of the target variable.

Linear regression is done if the target variable is an interval variable. In linear regression, the model predicts the mean of the target variable at the given values of the input variables.

Logistic regression is done if the target variable is a discrete variable. In logistic regression, the model predicts the probability of a particular level(s) of the target variable at the given values of the input variables. Because the predictions are probabilities, which are bounded by 0 and 1 and are not linear in this space, the probabilities must be transformed in order to be adequately modeled. The most common transformation for a binary target is the logit transformation. Probit and complementary log-log transformations are also available in the Regression node.

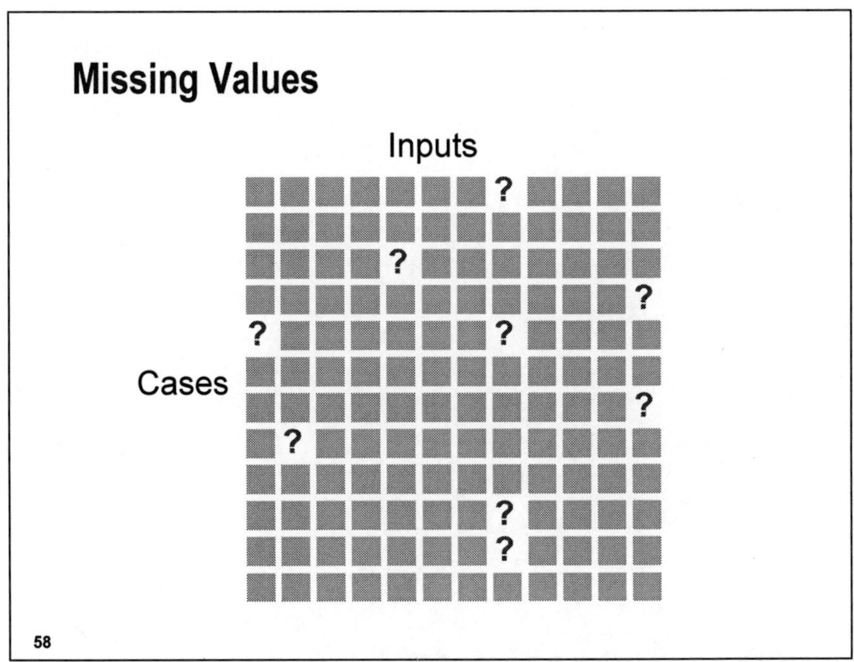


Regression uses only full cases in the model. This means that any case, or observation, that has a missing value will be excluded from consideration when building the model. When there are many potential input variables to be considered, an unacceptably high loss of data could result. Therefore when possible, missing values should be imputed prior to running a regression model.

Other reasons for imputing missing values include the following:

- Decision trees handle missing values directly, whereas regression and neural network models ignore all observations with missing values on any of the input variables. It is more appropriate to compare models built on the same set of observations. Therefore, before doing a regression or building a neural network model, you should perform data replacement, particularly if you plan to compare the results to results obtained from a decision tree model.
- If the missing values are in some way related to each other or to the target variable, the models created without those observations might be biased.
- If missing values are not imputed during the modeling process, observations with missing values cannot be scored with the score code built from the models.

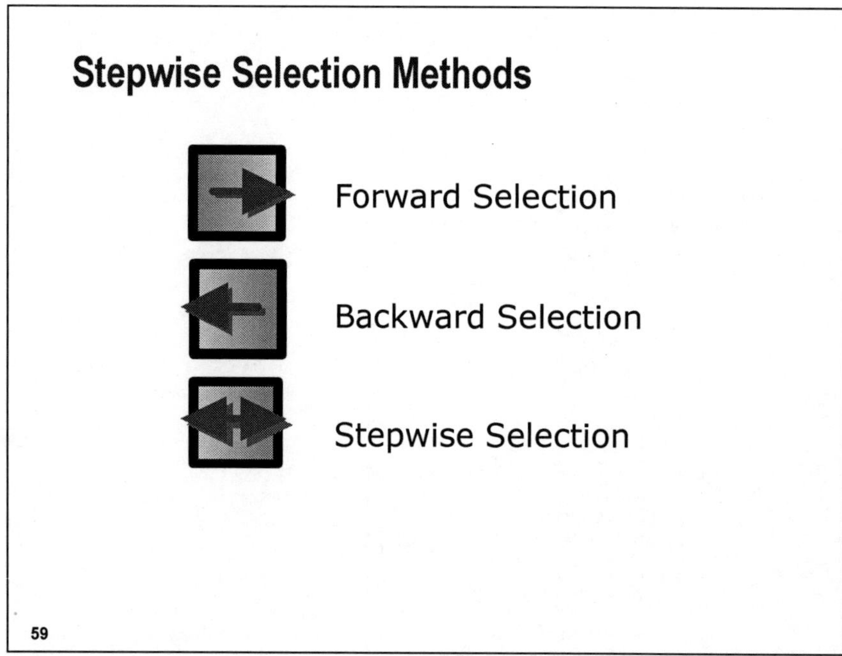

Stepwise Selection Methods
Forward Selection
Backward Selection
Stepwise Selection
59


There are three variable selection methods available in the Regression node of SAS Enterprise Miner.

Forward selects the best one-variable model first. Then it selects the best two variables among those that contain the first selected variable. This process continues until it reaches the point where no additional variables have a *p*-value less than the specified entry *p*-value.

Backward starts with the full model. Next, the variable that is least significant, given the other variables, is removed from the model. This process continues until all of the remaining variables have a *p*-value less than the specified stay *p*-value.

Stepwise is a modification of the forward selection method. The difference is that variables already in the model do not necessarily stay there. After each variable is entered into the model, this method looks at all the variables already included in the model and deletes any variable that is not significant at the specified level. The process ends when none of the variables outside the model has a *p*-value less than the specified entry value and every variable in the model is significant at the specified stay value.

The specified *p*-values are also known as *significance levels*.

# Imputation, Transformation, and Regression

## Understanding and Using Data Replacement

1. Add an Impute node to the diagram and connect it to the **Data Partition** node. Your new diagram should look like this:

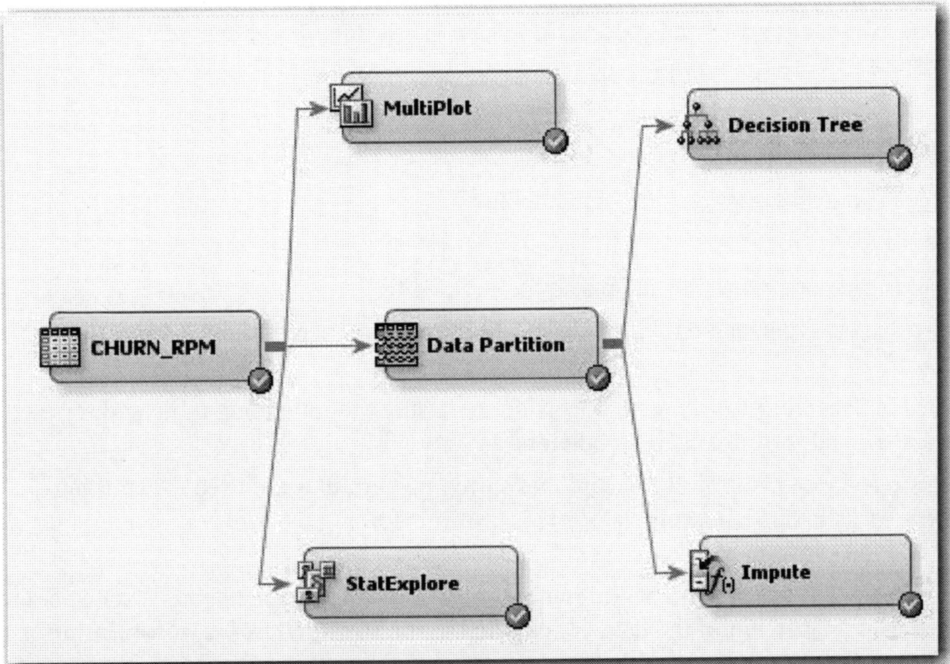


2. Select the **Impute** node in the workspace and examine the Properties panel.

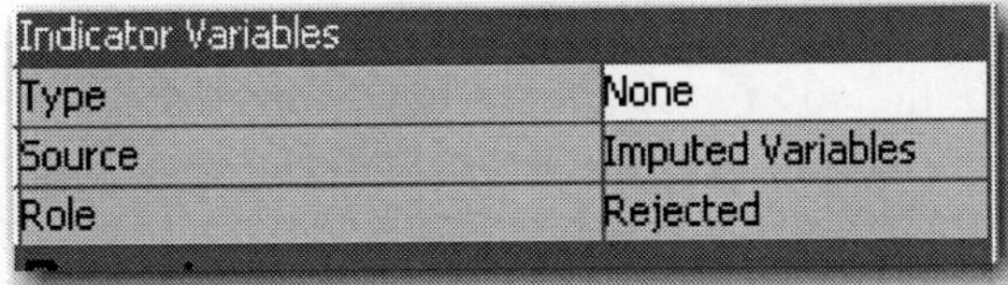

| Indicator Variables | |
|---|---|
| Type | None |
| Source | Imputed Variables |
| Role | Rejected |

3. In the Score section of the Properties panel, use the drop-down menu to change the value of the Indicator Variable type to **Unique**.

4. Change the Indicator Variable Role to **Input**.

   This requests the creation of new variables, each having a prefix **M_** followed by the original variable name. These new variables have a value of 1 when an observation has a missing value for the associated variable and 0 otherwise. If the "missingness" of a variable is related to the response variable, the regression and the neural network model can use these newly created indicator variables to identify observations that had missing values originally.

5. Examine the Interval Variables and Class Variables sections of the Properties panel.

| Class Variables | |
|---|---|
| Default Input Method | Count |
| Default Target Method | None |
| Normalize Values | Yes |
| **Interval Variables** | |
| Default Input Method | Mean |
| Default Target Method | None |

This shows that the default imputation method for interval variables is the mean. By default, imputation for class variables is done using the most frequently occurring level (also referred to as the *count* or the *mode*). If the most commonly occurring value is missing, it uses the second most frequently occurring level in the sample.

Click in the cell showing the default input method for interval variables. SAS Enterprise Miner provides the following methods for imputing missing values for interval variables:

- Mean – uses the arithmetic average. This is the default.
- Median – uses the $50^{th}$ percentile.
- Mid-Range – uses the maximum plus the minimum divided by 2.
- Distribution – calculates replacement values based on the random percentiles of the variable's distribution.
- Tree – estimates replacement values with a decision tree using the remaining input and rejected variables that have a status of use as the predictors.
- Tree Surrogates – is the same as above except that surrogate variables are used for splitting whenever a split variable has a missing value. This prevents forcing everyone with a missing value for a variable into the same node.
- Mid-Minimum Spacing – uses the mid-minimum spacing statistic. To calculate this statistic, the data is trimmed using *N* percent of the data as specified in the **Proportion for mid-minimum spacing** entry field. By default, 90% of the data is used to trim the original data. In other words, 5% of the data is dropped from each end of the distribution. The mid-range is calculated from this trimmed data.
- Tukey's Biweight, Huber, and Andrew's Wave – are robust M-estimators of location. This class of estimators minimizes functions of the deviations of the observations from the estimate that are more general than the sum of squared deviations or the sum of absolute deviations. M-estimators generalize the idea of the maximum-likelihood estimator of the location parameter in a specified distribution.
- Default Constant Value – enables you to set a default value to be imputed for some or all variables.
- None – turns off the imputation for interval variables.

Click in the cell that shows the default input method for class variables. SAS Enterprise Miner provides several of the same methods for imputing missing values for class variables including distribution, tree, tree surrogate, default constant value, and none.

6. Take the default as the imputation method for class variables and choose tree for interval variables..

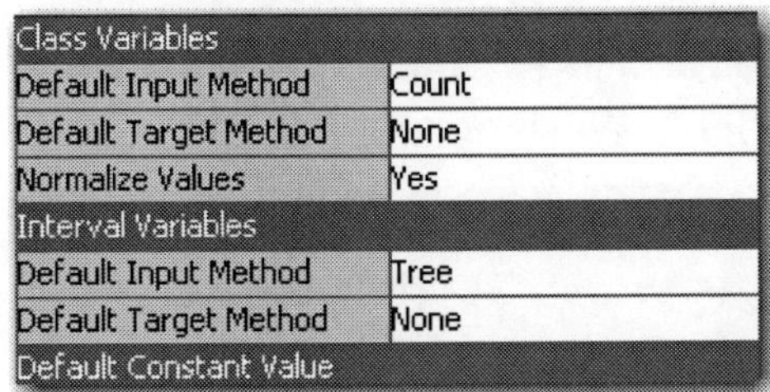

| Class Variables | |
|---|---|
| Default Input Method | Count |
| Default Target Method | None |
| Normalize Values | Yes |
| Interval Variables | |
| Default Input Method | Tree |
| Default Target Method | None |
| Default Constant Value | |

Regardless of the values set in this section, you can select any imputation method for any variable. The Properties panel merely controls the default settings. It was noted earlier that this data contains a variable that records the reason that the individual requested the loan: debt consolidation or home improvement. There are also a few missing values for this variable, **Reason**. Suppose you make a business decision to recode these missing values to **Other**.

7. Note the Default Constant Value section of the Properties panel. Type **Other** in the field for character values.

   Examine the other options available in the Properties Panel. The Non Missing Variables property is set to **No** by default. This indicates that imputation will not be done for variables that have no missing values in the input data set. In addition, missing value indicator variables will not be created for those variables that are not imputed. While this prevents the creation of unary missing value indicator variables, it also can create a scoring issue if the data to be scored contains missing values where the training data has none. This can degrade model performance if this happens often.

   When you select **Tree** as an imputation method, you have options to control the growth of the trees. You can view these options by selecting the ... button in the Tree Imputation row of the Method Options section in the Properties panel.

8. Run the diagram from the Impute node and view the results.

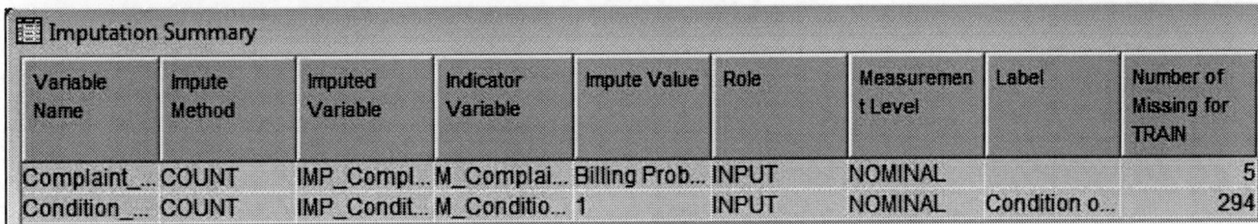

Imputation Summary

| Variable Name | Impute Method | Imputed Variable | Indicator Variable | Impute Value | Role | Measurement Level | Label | Number of Missing for TRAIN |
|---|---|---|---|---|---|---|---|---|
| Complaint_... | COUNT | IMP_Compl... | M_Complai... | Billing Prob... | INPUT | NOMINAL | | 5 |
| Condition_... | COUNT | IMP_Condit... | M_Conditio... | 1 | INPUT | NOMINAL | Condition o... | 294 |

   The Imputation Summary shows that there were 2 variables with missing values that were imputed.

9. Close the Impute node results and return to the diagram.

## Performing Variable Transformations

1. Select the data source node and then select the ellipse button next to **Variables**. Now select all interval variables and then the **Explore** button to produce the plots below.

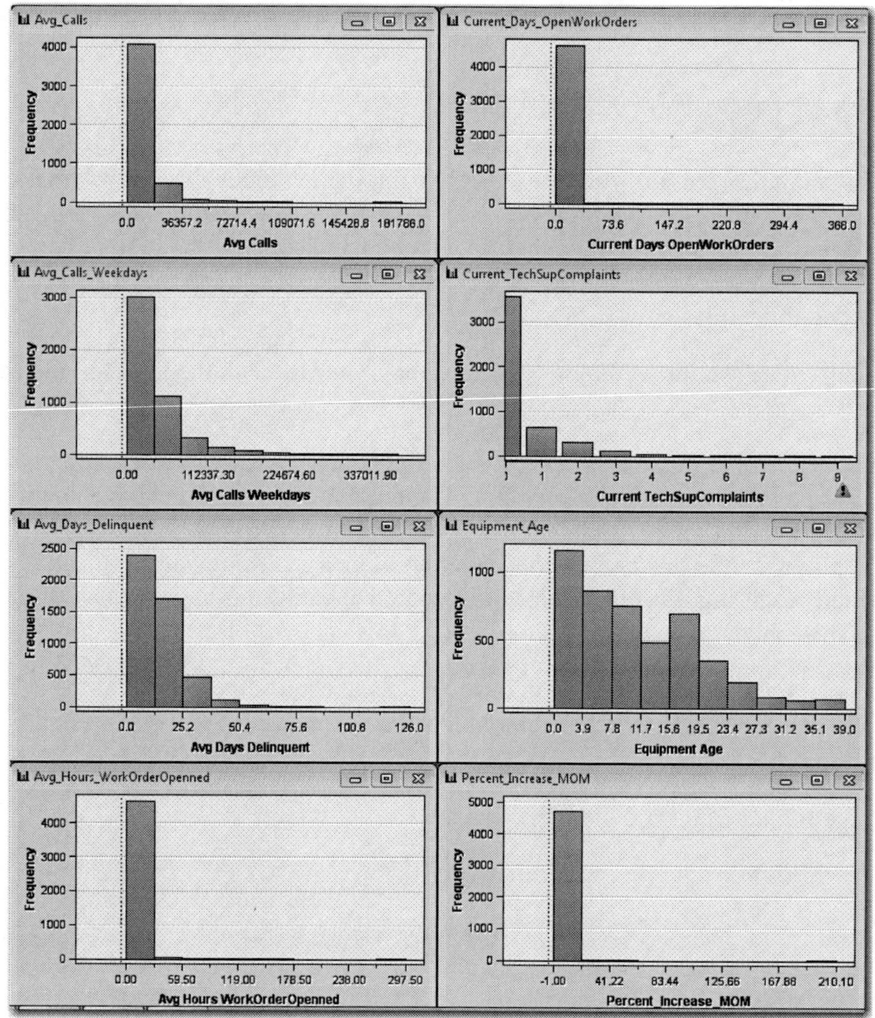

Some input variables have highly skewed distributions. In highly skewed distributions, a small percentage of the points can have a great deal of influence. On occasion, performing a transformation on an input variable can yield a better fitting model. This section demonstrates how to perform some common transformations.

2. Add a Transform Variables node to the flow as shown below.

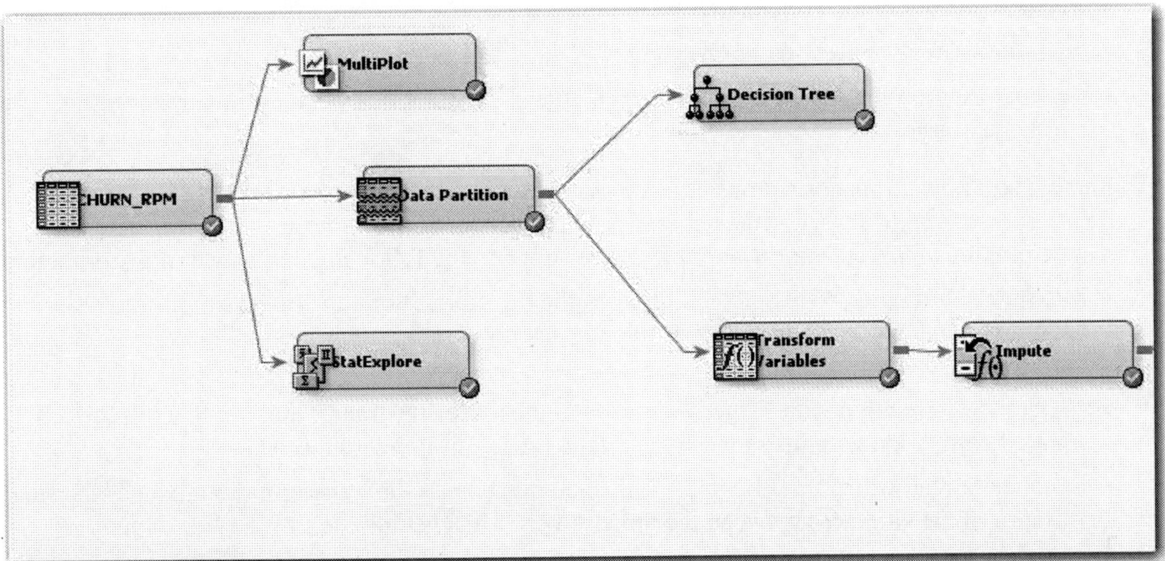


3. Select the **Transform Variables** node and examine the Properties panel.

| Default Methods | |
|---|---|
| Interval Inputs | None |
| Interval Targets | None |
| Class Inputs | None |
| Class Targets | None |
| Treat Missing as Level | No |

By default, no transformations are done.

4. Select ... in the Variables row of the Properties panel.

5. Click in the Method column of any interval variable row in the Variables window.

The Transform Variables node enables you to rapidly transform interval-valued variables using standard transformations such as the log, square root, inverse, and square.

In addition to these standard transformations, you can collapse an interval variable into a grouping variable that creates bins for the values of an interval variable. This can be done in several different ways:

- Bucket – creates cutoffs at equally spaced intervals.
- Quantile – creates bins with approximately equal frequencies.
- Optimal Binning for Relationship to Target – creates cutoffs that yield optimal relationship to target (for binary targets).

Finally, best power transformations are also available for interval variables. These best power transformations are a subset of the general class of transformations that are known as *Box-Cox transformations*. The Transform Variables node supports the following best power transformations:

- Maximize Normality – This method chooses the transformation that yields sample quantiles that are closest to the theoretical quantiles of a normal distribution. This method requires an interval variable.
- Maximize Correlation with Target – This method chooses the transformation that has the best squared correlation with the target. This method requires an interval target.
- Equalize Spread with Target Levels – This method chooses the transformation that has the smallest variance of the variances between the target levels. This method requires a class target.
- Optimal Maximum Equalize Spread with Target Level – This method chooses the transformation that equalizes spread with target levels. This method requires a class target.

The Transform Variables node can also be used for class variables. The transformations available for class variables are to group rare levels or to create indicator variables.

You can also create your own transformations by building equations for these using the Formula Builder.

You can examine the distributions of variables within the Transform Variables node by highlighting the row for the variable(s) of interest and selecting. While holding the CTRL key, select the variables that are highlighted above in the table.

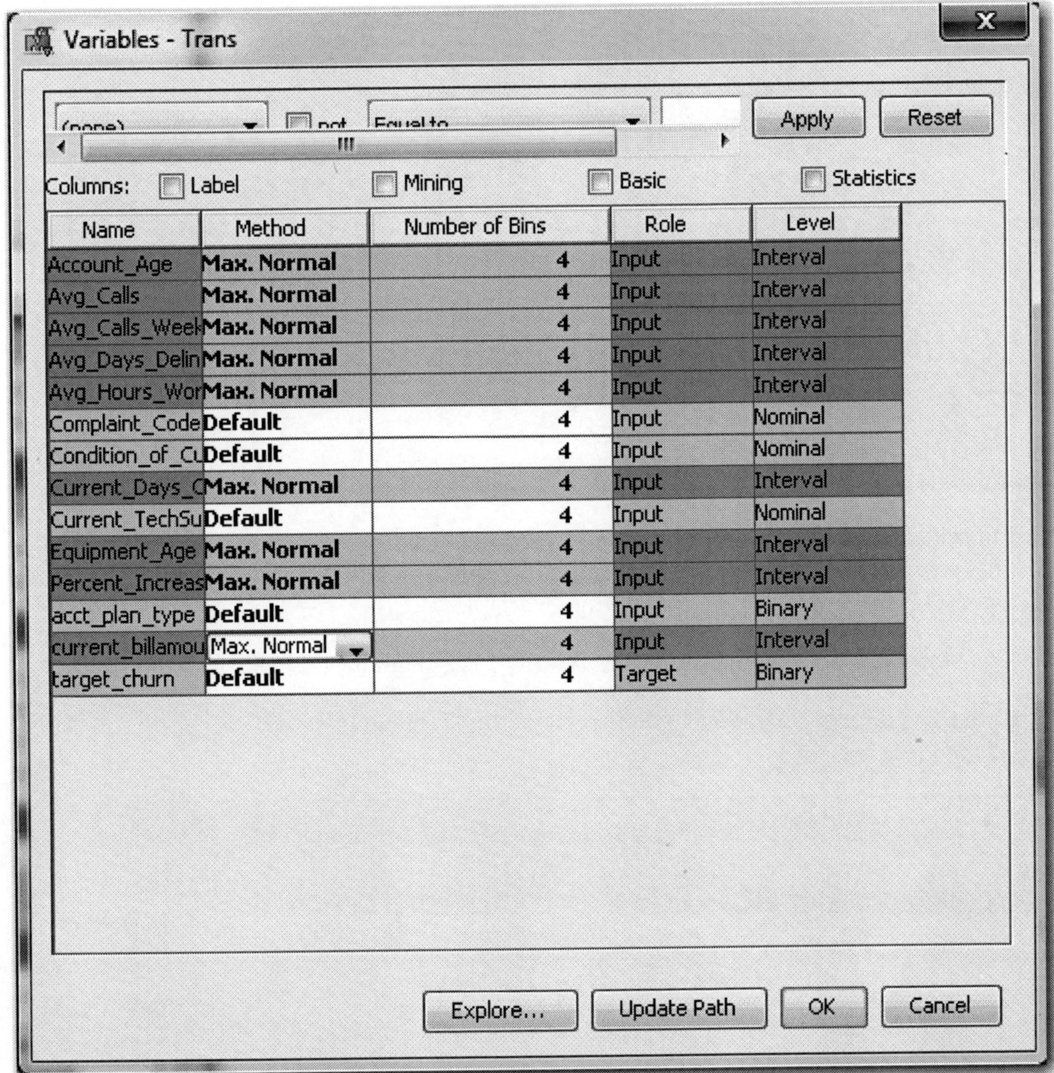


6. When they have been selected, release the CTRL key.
7. Click in the Method column of one of the selected rows and select **Max. Normal**.
8. Select OK to close the **Variables - Trans** window.
9. Run the diagram from the **Transform Variables** node and view the results.

10. Scroll down in the **Output** window to view the transformations that have been done.

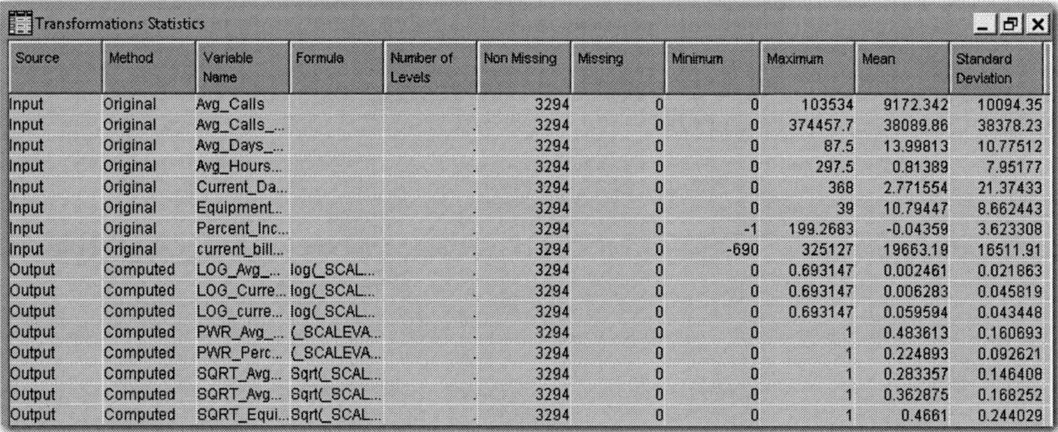

Transformations Statistics

| Source | Method | Variable Name | Formula | Number of Levels | Non Missing | Missing | Minimum | Maximum | Mean | Standard Deviation |
|---|---|---|---|---|---|---|---|---|---|---|
| Input | Original | Avg_Calls | | . | 3294 | 0 | 0 | 103534 | 9172.342 | 10094.35 |
| Input | Original | Avg_Calls_... | | . | 3294 | 0 | 0 | 374457.7 | 38089.86 | 38378.23 |
| Input | Original | Avg_Days_... | | . | 3294 | 0 | 0 | 87.5 | 13.99813 | 10.77512 |
| Input | Original | Avg_Hours... | | . | 3294 | 0 | 0 | 297.5 | 0.81389 | 7.95177 |
| Input | Original | Current_Da... | | . | 3294 | 0 | 0 | 368 | 2.771554 | 21.37433 |
| Input | Original | Equipment... | | . | 3294 | 0 | 0 | 39 | 10.79447 | 8.662443 |
| Input | Original | Percent_Inc... | | . | 3294 | 0 | -1 | 199.2683 | -0.04359 | 3.623308 |
| Input | Original | current_bill... | | . | 3294 | 0 | -690 | 325127 | 19663.19 | 16511.91 |
| Output | Computed | LOG_Avg_... | log(_SCAL... | . | 3294 | 0 | 0 | 0.693147 | 0.002461 | 0.021863 |
| Output | Computed | LOG_Curre... | log(_SCAL... | . | 3294 | 0 | 0 | 0.693147 | 0.006283 | 0.045819 |
| Output | Computed | LOG_curre... | log(_SCAL... | . | 3294 | 0 | 0 | 0.693147 | 0.059594 | 0.043448 |
| Output | Computed | PWR_Avg_... | (_SCALEVA... | . | 3294 | 0 | 0 | 1 | 0.483613 | 0.160693 |
| Output | Computed | PWR_Perc... | (_SCALEVA... | . | 3294 | 0 | 0 | 1 | 0.224893 | 0.092621 |
| Output | Computed | SQRT_Avg... | Sqrt(_SCAL... | . | 3294 | 0 | 0 | 1 | 0.283357 | 0.146408 |
| Output | Computed | SQRT_Avg... | Sqrt(_SCAL... | . | 3294 | 0 | 0 | 1 | 0.362875 | 0.168252 |
| Output | Computed | SQRT_Equi... | Sqrt(_SCAL... | . | 3294 | 0 | 0 | 1 | 0.4661 | 0.244029 |

Note that Enterprise Miner chose different transformations to achieve maximize normality. Also notice that the new transformed variables are named by Enterprise Miner and their role will be input. You can inspect the distribution of the transformed variables.

11. Close the Transform Variables node results and return to the diagram.

12. Be sure that the **Transform Variables** node is selected in the diagram and select [...] in the **Exported Data** row of the Properties panel.

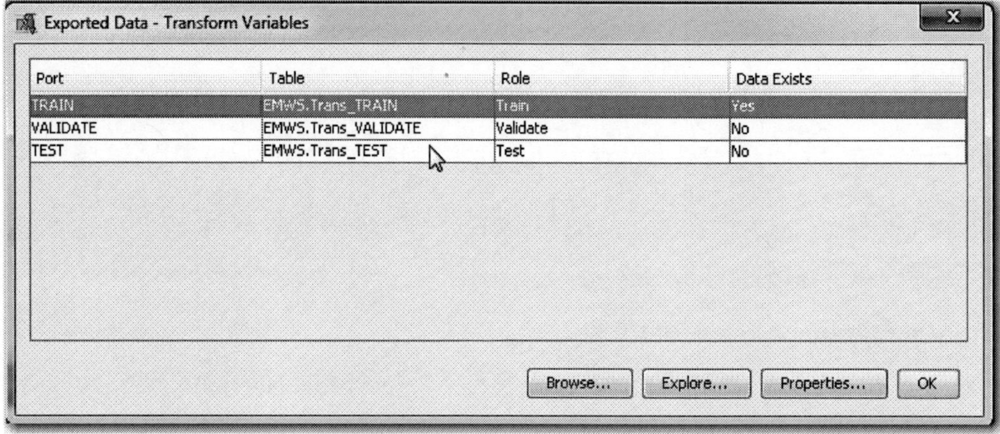

Exported Data - Transform Variables

| Port | Table | Role | Data Exists |
|---|---|---|---|
| TRAIN | EMWS.Trans_TRAIN | Train | Yes |
| VALIDATE | EMWS.Trans_VALIDATE | Validate | No |
| TEST | EMWS.Trans_TEST | Test | No |



13. Highlight the row for the training data table in the window and select [Explore...].

14. In the Explore window, select [Plot...] under the **Actions Tab**.

15. Select **Histogram** as the type of chart.

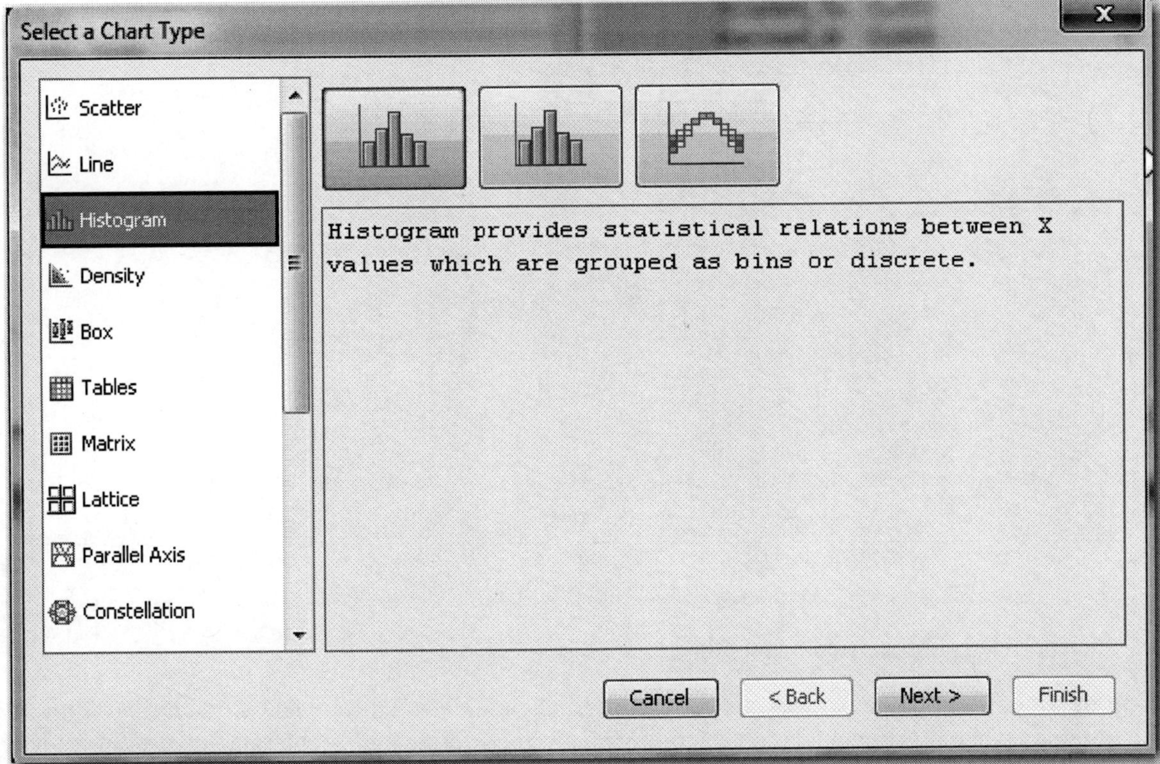


16. Select Next >.

17. Change the role of **SQRT_Avg_Days_Delinquent** to **X**.

18. Select Finish.

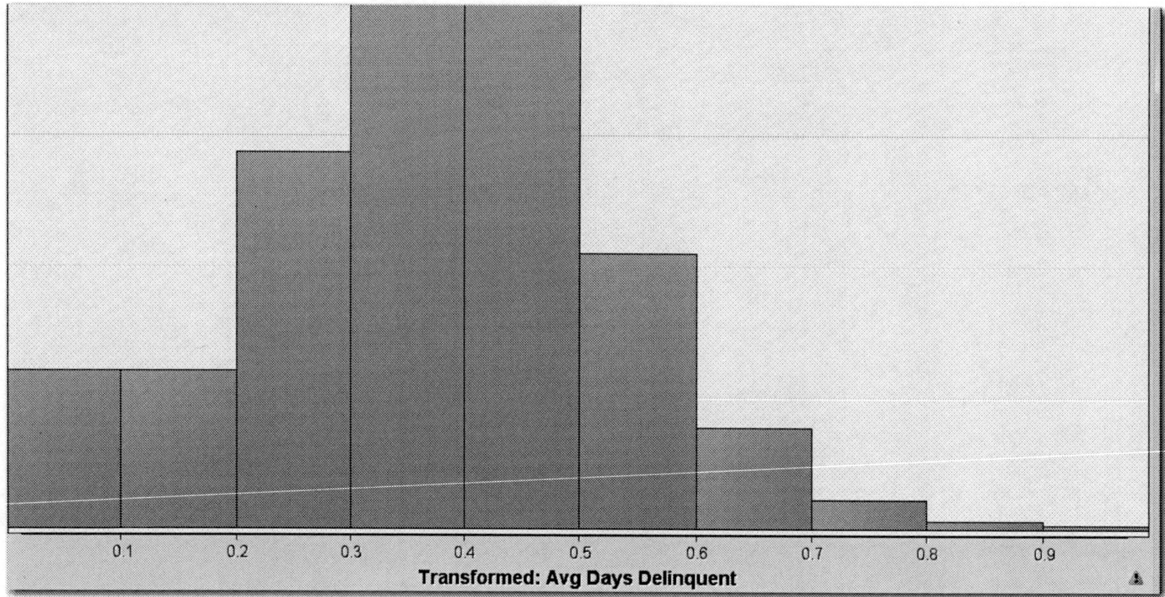


The variable is less skewed than before.

It might be appropriate at times to keep the original variable and the created variable. This typically is **not** done when the original variable and the transformed variable have the same measurement level. The default behavior of SAS Enterprise Miner is to hide and reject the original variables. This behavior can be changed in the Properties panel.

19. Close the Explore and Exported data windows when you are finished examining the distribution of variables.

## Fitting a Regression Model

1. Add a **Regression** node and a **Model Comparison** node to the diagram and connect them as shown.

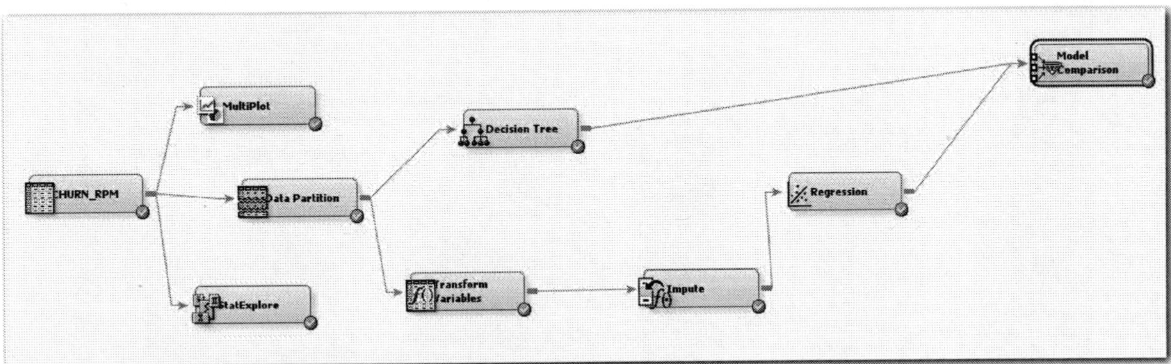


2. Select the **Regression** node in the diagram and examine the Properties panel.

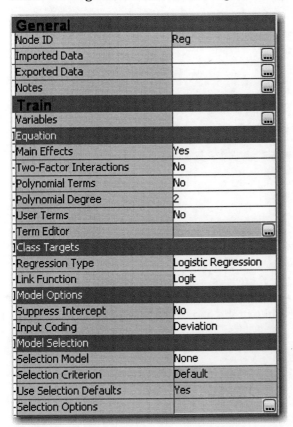

| Property | Value |
|---|---|
| **General** | |
| Node ID | Reg |
| Imported Data | ... |
| Exported Data | ... |
| Notes | ... |
| **Train** | |
| Variables | ... |
| Equation | |
| -Main Effects | Yes |
| -Two-Factor Interactions | No |
| -Polynomial Terms | No |
| -Polynomial Degree | 2 |
| -User Terms | No |
| -Term Editor | ... |
| Class Targets | |
| -Regression Type | Logistic Regression |
| -Link Function | Logit |
| Model Options | |
| -Suppress Intercept | No |
| -Input Coding | Deviation |
| Model Selection | |
| -Selection Model | None |
| -Selection Criterion | Default |
| -Use Selection Defaults | Yes |
| -Selection Options | ... |

3. Select [...] in the **Variables** row of the Properties panel.

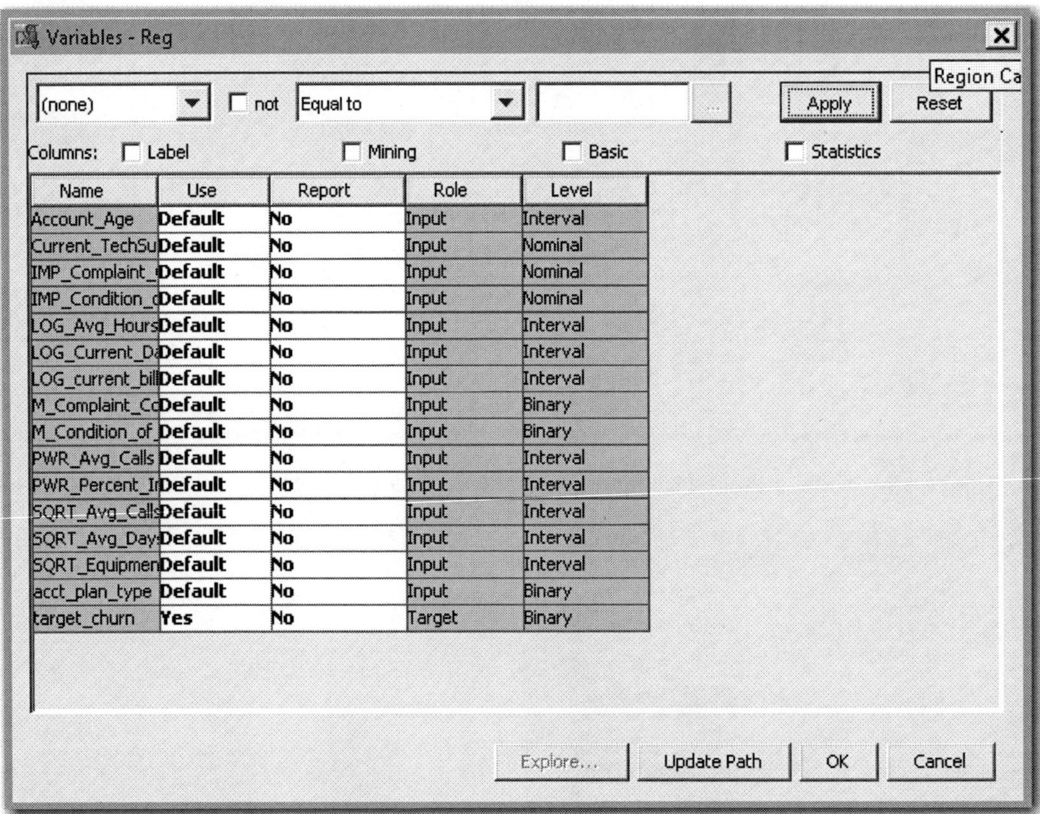


| Name | Use | Report | Role | Level |
|---|---|---|---|---|
| Account_Age | Default | No | Input | Interval |
| Current_TechSu | Default | No | Input | Nominal |
| IMP_Complaint_ | Default | No | Input | Nominal |
| IMP_Condition_ | Default | No | Input | Nominal |
| LOG_Avg_Hours | Default | No | Input | Interval |
| LOG_Current_D | Default | No | Input | Interval |
| LOG_current_bil | Default | No | Input | Interval |
| M_Complaint_C | Default | No | Input | Binary |
| M_Condition_of_ | Default | No | Input | Binary |
| PWR_Avg_Calls | Default | No | Input | Interval |
| PWR_Percent_I | Default | No | Input | Interval |
| SQRT_Avg_Calls | Default | No | Input | Interval |
| SQRT_Avg_Day | Default | No | Input | Interval |
| SQRT_Equipmen | Default | No | Input | Interval |
| acct_plan_type | Default | No | Input | Binary |
| target_churn | Yes | No | Target | Binary |

Note that the pre-transformed variables do not appear in the variable list because the default behavior is to hide those variables.

4. Select [OK] to close the Variables window.

Examine the Class Targets section of the Properties panel. Based on the binary target variable, the **Regression** node is automatically set to do a logistic regression with a logit transformation. If you click on each of these, you see that the node can also do linear regression and can use two alternate forms of transformations for the logistic regression: the probit and the complementary log-log transformations.

5. Examine the model selection options of the Properties panel. Change the Selection Model option from None to **Stepwise** using the drop-down menu and Use Model Defaults to **No**.

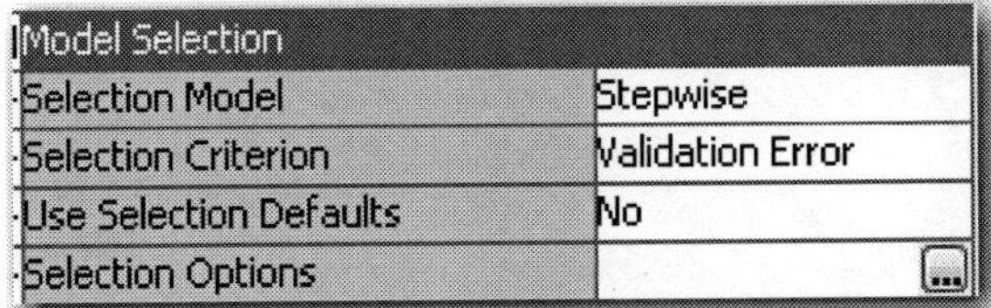


Select the Selection Options button to obtain the window below, this allows you to make changes in the selection priperties.

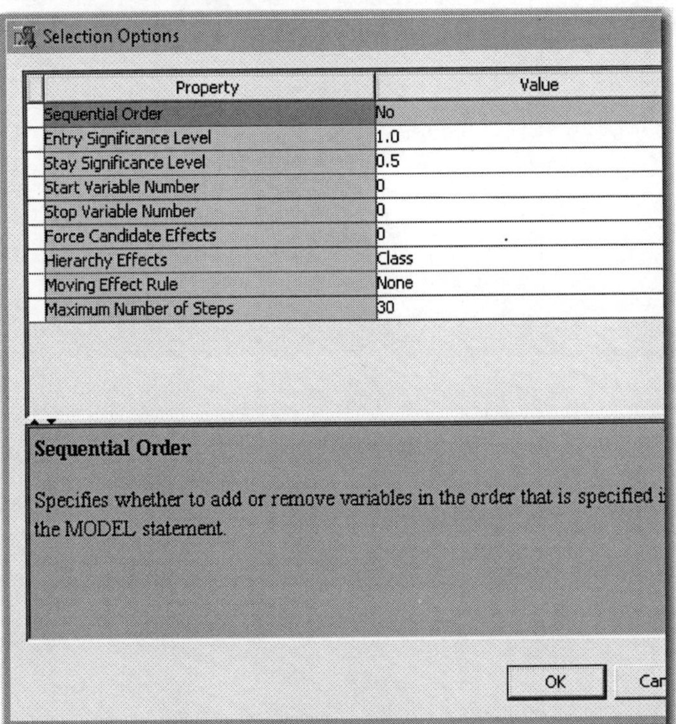


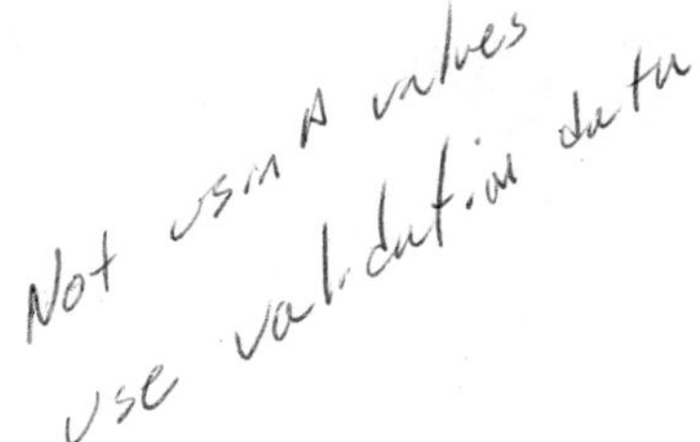

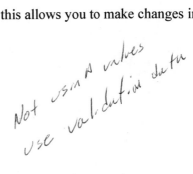

When you specify a selection criterion in this section, the node first performs the effect selection process, which generates a set of candidate models corresponding to each step in the process. Effect selection is done based on the Entry and/or Stay significance levels, which are 0.05 by default, change these to 1 and .5 respectively and change the Maximum Number of Steps to 30 These changes will generate more models from which to choose the “best” model. Therefore, by default, after the effect selection process terminates, the final candidate model is chosen as the final model. If you want to use the validation data set to choose from among the candidate models, you would need to change the Selection Criterion property.

6. To choose the candidate model that minimizes the validation error rate, change the Selection Criterion option from Default to **Validation Error**.

   The equation section of the Properties panel enables the user to include all two-way interaction terms for class variables and all cross-product and polynomial terms for interval variables in the model. It also enables the user to identify other specific higher-order terms to be included in the model. This allows for maximum flexibility when desired.

7. Run the flow from the Regression node and examine the results.

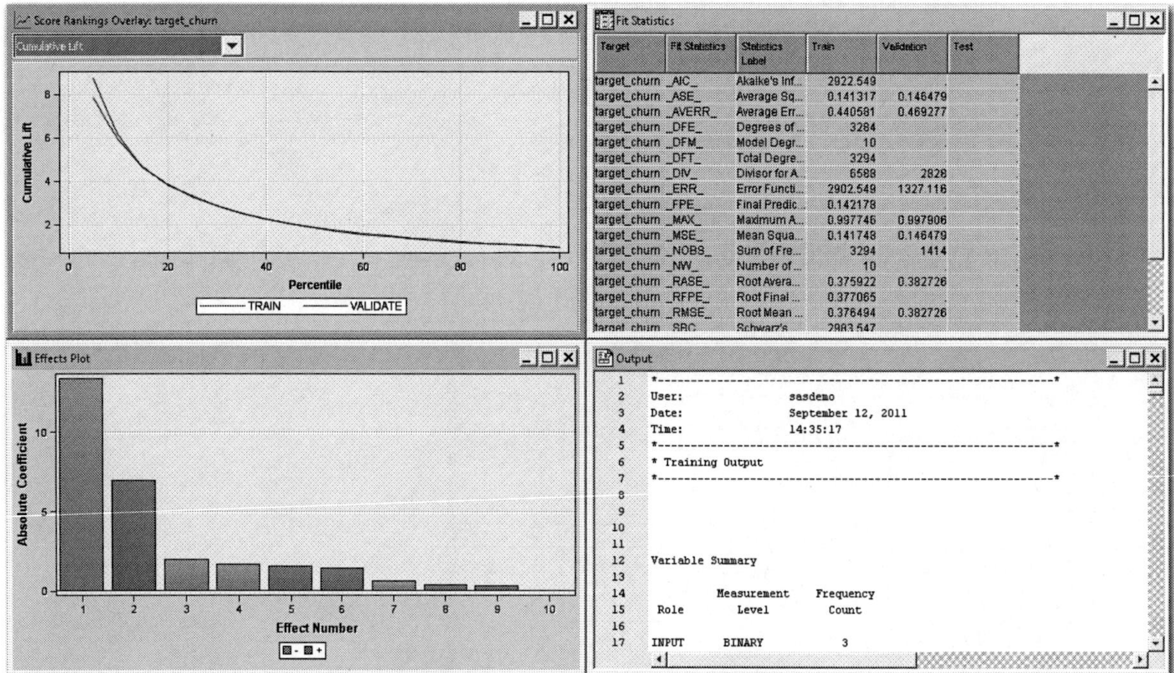


8. Maximize and examine the effects plot.

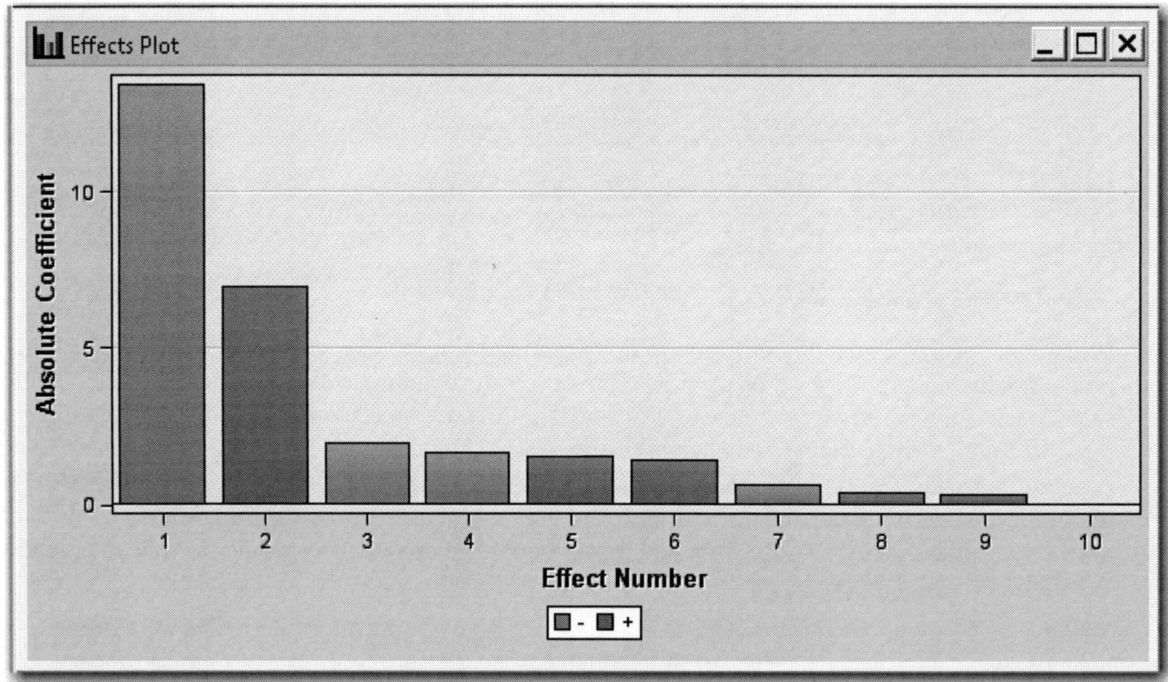


The plot shows the model parameter estimates. When you hold your cursor over a bar in the plot, the information about the coefficient and the variable it represents is displayed

9. Examine the Fit Statistics window in the results.

Fit Statistics

| Target | Fit Statistics | Statistics Label | Train | Validation | Test |
|---|---|---|---|---|---|
| target_churn | _AIC_ | Akaike's Inf... | 2922.549 | . | |
| target_churn | _ASE_ | Average Sq... | 0.141317 | 0.146479 | |
| target_churn | _AVERR_ | Average Err... | 0.440581 | 0.469277 | |
| target_churn | _DFE_ | Degrees of ... | 3284 | . | |
| target_churn | _DFM_ | Model Degr... | 10 | . | |
| target_churn | _DFT_ | Total Degre... | 3294 | . | |
| target_churn | _DIV_ | Divisor for A... | 6588 | 2828 | |
| target_churn | _ERR_ | Error Functi... | 2902.549 | 1327.116 | |
| target_churn | _FPE_ | Final Predic... | 0.142178 | . | |
| target_churn | _MAX_ | Maximum A... | 0.997746 | 0.997906 | |
| target_churn | _MSE_ | Mean Squa... | 0.141748 | 0.146479 | |
| target_churn | _NOBS_ | Sum of Fre... | 3294 | 1414 | |
| target_churn | _NW_ | Number of ... | 10 | . | |
| target_churn | _RASE_ | Root Avera... | 0.375922 | 0.382726 | |
| target_churn | _RFPE_ | Root Final ... | 0.377065 | . | |
| target_churn | _RMSE_ | Root Mean ... | 0.376494 | 0.382726 | |
| target_churn | _SBC_ | Schwarz's ... | 2983.547 | . | |
| target_churn | _SSE_ | Sum of Squ... | 930.9976 | 414.243 | |
| target_churn | _SUMW_ | Sum of Cas... | 6588 | 2828 | |
| target_churn | _MISC_ | Misclassific... | 0.381299 | 0.379774 | |
| target_churn | _PROF_ | Total Profit f... | 5262.238 | 2240.342 | |
| target_churn | _APROF_ | Average Pr... | 1.597522 | 1.5844 | |

The Statistics tab lists fit statistics for the training data and validation data analyzed with the regression model. In this example, you have only training and validation data sets.

10. Close the regression results and select the **Model Comparison** node. Change the properties panel to match the panel shown below. Note we are changing the **Selection Statistic** and **Selection Table**.

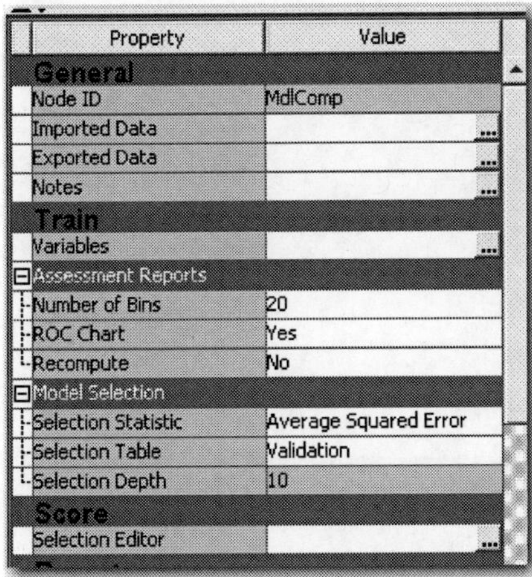

| Property | Value |
|---|---|
| **General** | |
| Node ID | MdlComp |
| Imported Data | ... |
| Exported Data | ... |
| Notes | ... |
| **Train** | |
| Variables | ... |
| Assessment Reports | |
| Number of Bins | 20 |
| ROC Chart | Yes |
| Recompute | No |
| Model Selection | |
| Selection Statistic | Average Squared Error |
| Selection Table | Validation |
| Selection Depth | 10 |
| **Score** | |
| Selection Editor | ... |

11. Run the flow from the Model Comparison node and view the results.

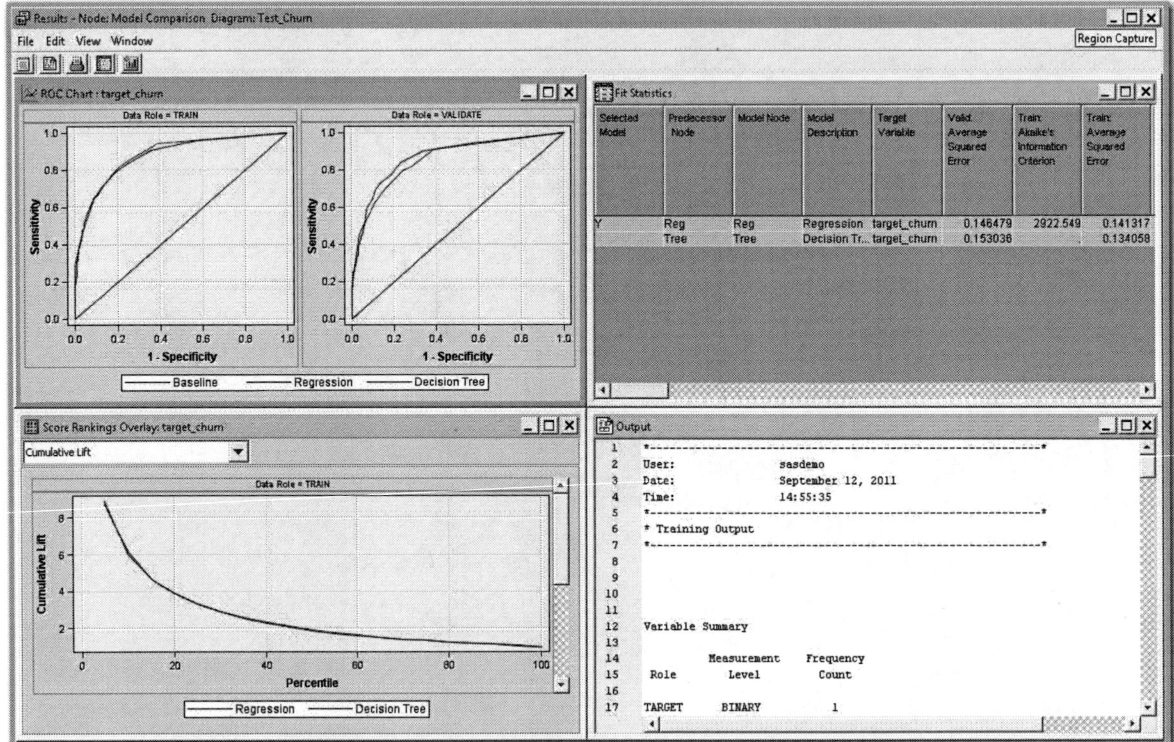


Focus on the lift chart for the validation data.

12. Maximize the Score Ranking Overlay window and examine the Cumulative Lift Plot

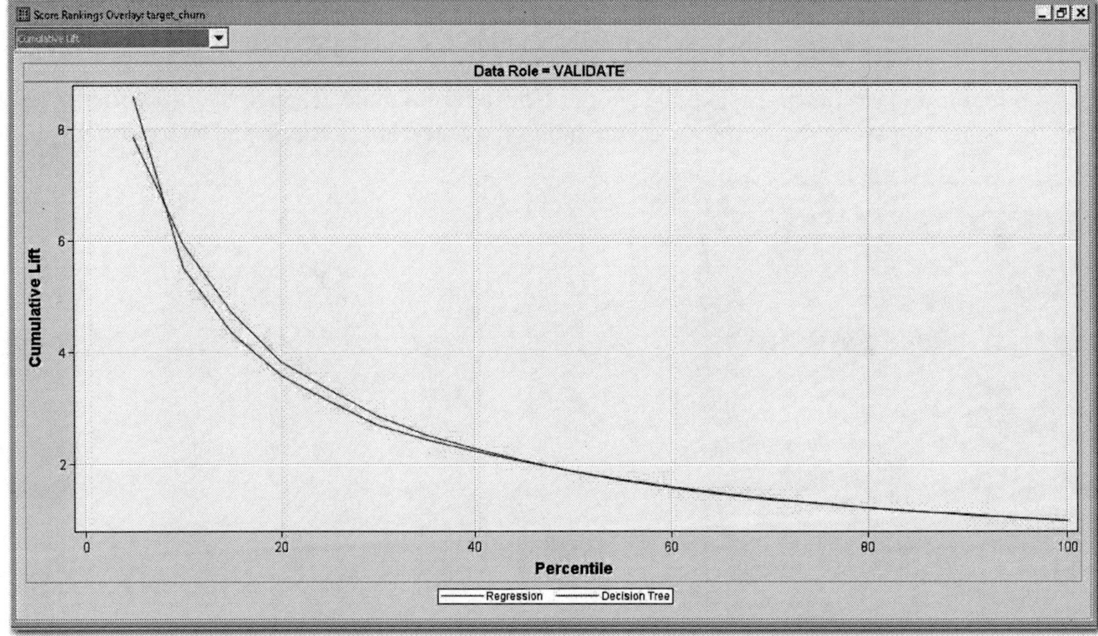


The regression model outperforms the decision tree mostly throughout the graph on the validation data.

13. Maximize the output panel and examine the results.

Fit Statistics
Model Selection based on Valid: Average Squared Error (_VASE_)

| Selected Model | Model Node | Model Description | Valid: Average Squared Error | Train: Average Squared Error | Train: Misclassification Rate | Valid: Misclassification Rate |
|---|---|---|---|---|---|---|
| Y | Reg | Regression | 0.14648 | 0.14132 | 0.38130 | 0.37977 |
| | Tree | Decision Tree | 0.15304 | 0.13406 | 0.37432 | 0.38967 |

From the Output report we see the selected model is based on validation average squared error..

# 1.5 Introduction to Neural Networks (Self-Study)

## Objectives

- Define a neural network.
- List the components of a neural network.
- Define an activation function.
- Fit a neural network model.

62

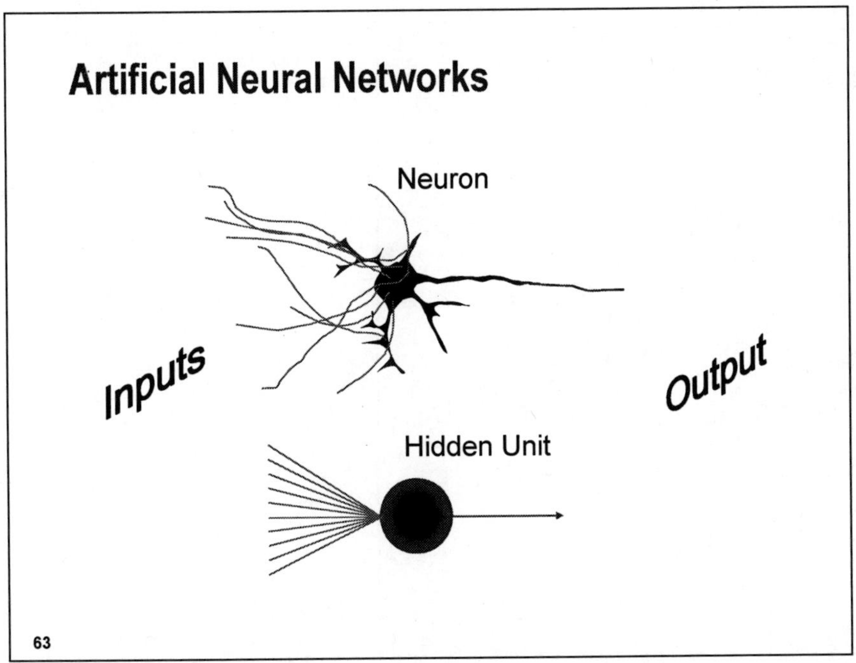


An organic neural network has 10 billion highly interconnected neurons acting in parallel. Each neuron can receive electrochemical signals (through synapses) from as many as 200,000 other neurons. These connections can be altered by environmental stimuli. If the right signal is received by the inputs, the neuron is activated and sends inhibitory or excitatory signals to other neurons.

In data analysis, artificial neural networks are a class of flexible nonlinear models used for supervised prediction problems. Yet, because of the ascribed analogy to neurophysiology, they are usually perceived to be more glamorous than other (statistical) prediction models.

The basic building blocks of an artificial neural network are called *hidden units*. Hidden units are modeled after the neuron. Each hidden unit receives a linear combination of input variables. The coefficients are called the (synaptic) weights. An activation function transforms the linear combinations and then outputs them to another unit that can then use them as inputs.

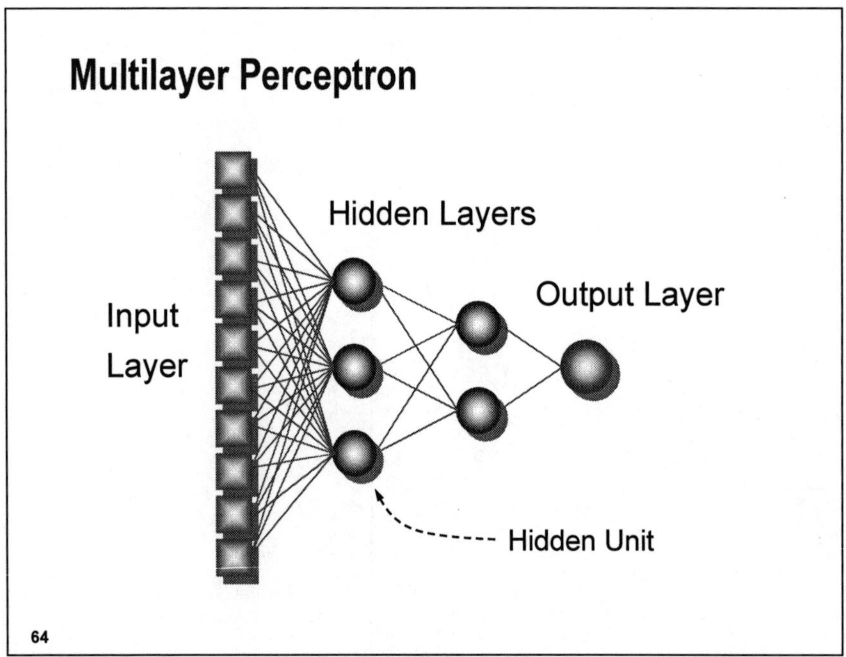


An *artificial* neural network is a flexible framework for specifying a variety of models. The most widely used type of neural network in data analysis is the *multilayer perceptron* (MLP). An MLP is a feed-forward network that is composed of an input layer, hidden layers composed of hidden units, and an output layer.

The input layer is composed of units that correspond to each input variable. For categorical inputs with *C* levels, *C*–1 input units will be created. Consequently, the number of input units might be greater than the number of inputs.

The hidden layers are composed of hidden units. Each hidden unit outputs a nonlinear function of a linear combination of its inputs, the *activation function.*

The output layer has units corresponding to the target. With multiple target variables or multiclass (>2) targets, there are multiple output units.

The network diagram is a representation of an underlying statistical model. The unknown parameters (weights and biases) correspond to the connections between the units.

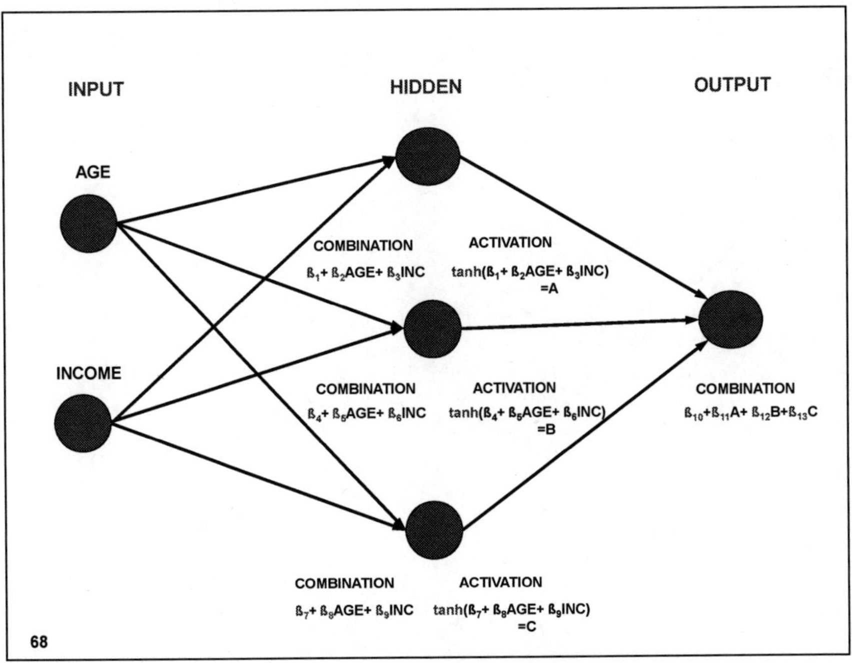


Each hidden unit outputs a nonlinear transformation of a linear combination of their inputs. The linear combination is the net input. The nonlinear transformation is the activation function. The activation functions that are used with MLPs are sigmoidal curves (surfaces).

A hidden layer can be thought of as a new (usually) lower-dimensional space that is a nonlinear combination of the previous layer. The output from the hidden units is linearly combined to form the input of the next layer. The combination of nonlinear surfaces gives MLPs their modeling flexibility.

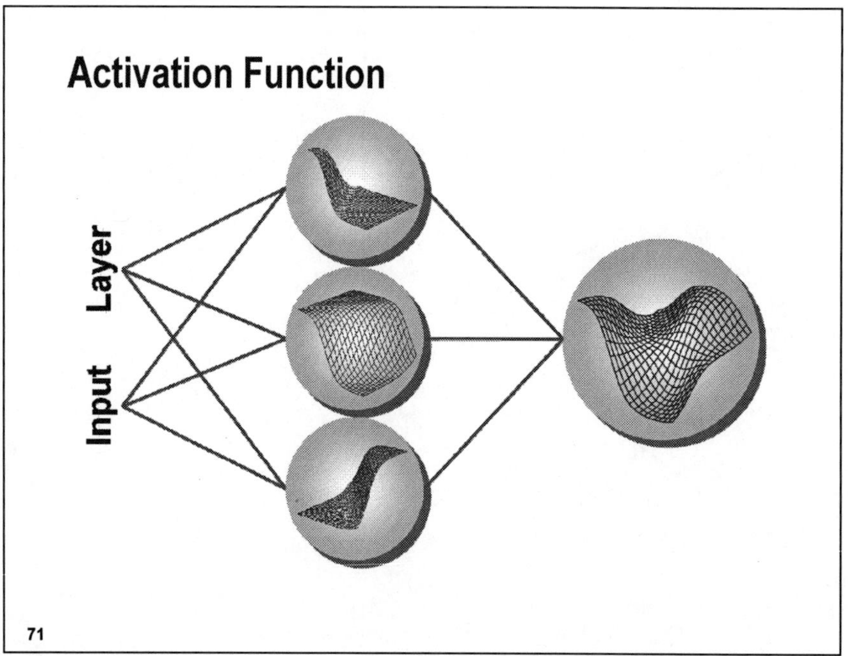


An output activation function is used to transform the output into a suitable scale for the expected value of the target. In statistics, this function is called the inverse *link function*. For binary targets, the logistic function is suitable because it constrains the output to be between zero and one (the expected value of a binary target is the posterior probability). The logistic function is sometimes used as the activation function for the hidden units as well. This sometimes gives the false impression that they are related. The choice of output activation function depends only on the scale of the target.

# Fitting a Neural Network Model

1. Add a **Neural Network** node to the diagram.

2. Connect the new node to the **Regression** and the **Model Comparison** node as shown below.

   The only variables that are passed to the **Neural Network** node are those that are selected by the **Regression** node. Thus, we are using the selection procedure in the **Regression** node to select variables for the **Neural Network** node. A **Decision Tree** or **Variable Selection** node could have been used.

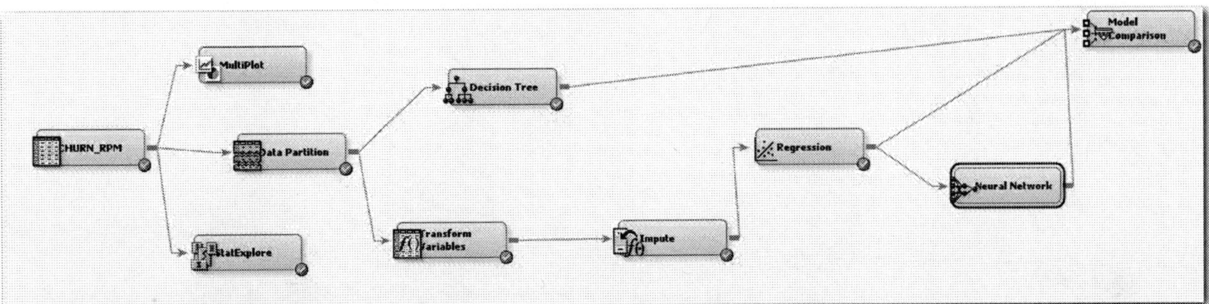


3. Select the **Neural Network** node.

4. Examine the properties of the node.

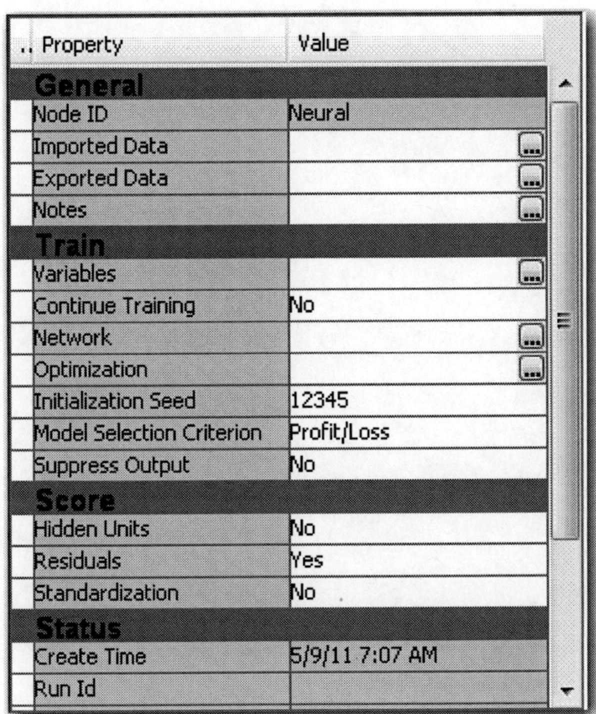

| Property | Value |
|---|---|
| **General** | |
| Node ID | Neural |
| Imported Data | ... |
| Exported Data | ... |
| Notes | ... |
| **Train** | |
| Variables | ... |
| Continue Training | No |
| Network | ... |
| Optimization | ... |
| Initialization Seed | 12345 |
| Model Selection Criterion | Profit/Loss |
| Suppress Output | No |
| **Score** | |
| Hidden Units | No |
| Residuals | Yes |
| Standardization | No |
| **Status** | |
| Create Time | 5/9/11 7:07 AM |
| Run Id | |

You can specify one of the following criteria for selecting the best model:

- Profit/Loss chooses the model that maximizes the profit or minimizes the loss for the cases in the validation data set.
- Misclassification Rate chooses the model that has the smallest misclassification rate for the validation data set.
- Average Error chooses the model that has the smallest average error for the validation data set.

5. Because you have not specified a profit/loss matrix for this example, change the Model Selection Criterion to **Average Error**.

The Continue Training property enables you to specify whether you want to use the current estimates as the starting values for training. When you set this property to **Yes**, the estimates from the previous run of the node are used as the initial values for training. To use this property, an estimates data set must have been created by the node before you set this property to **Yes**.

6. Examine the Optimization properties of the node, and select [...]. The training options include
   - the maximum number of iterations allowed during the neural network training. The permissible values are integers from 1 to 500. The default value is 50, change this value to 100.
   - the maximum amount of CPU time that you want to use during training. Permissible values are 5 minutes, 10 minutes, 30 minutes, 1 hour, 2 hours, 4 hours, or 7 hours. The default setting for the Maximum Time property is 4 hours.
   - the training technique, which is the methodology used to iterate from the starting values to a solution.

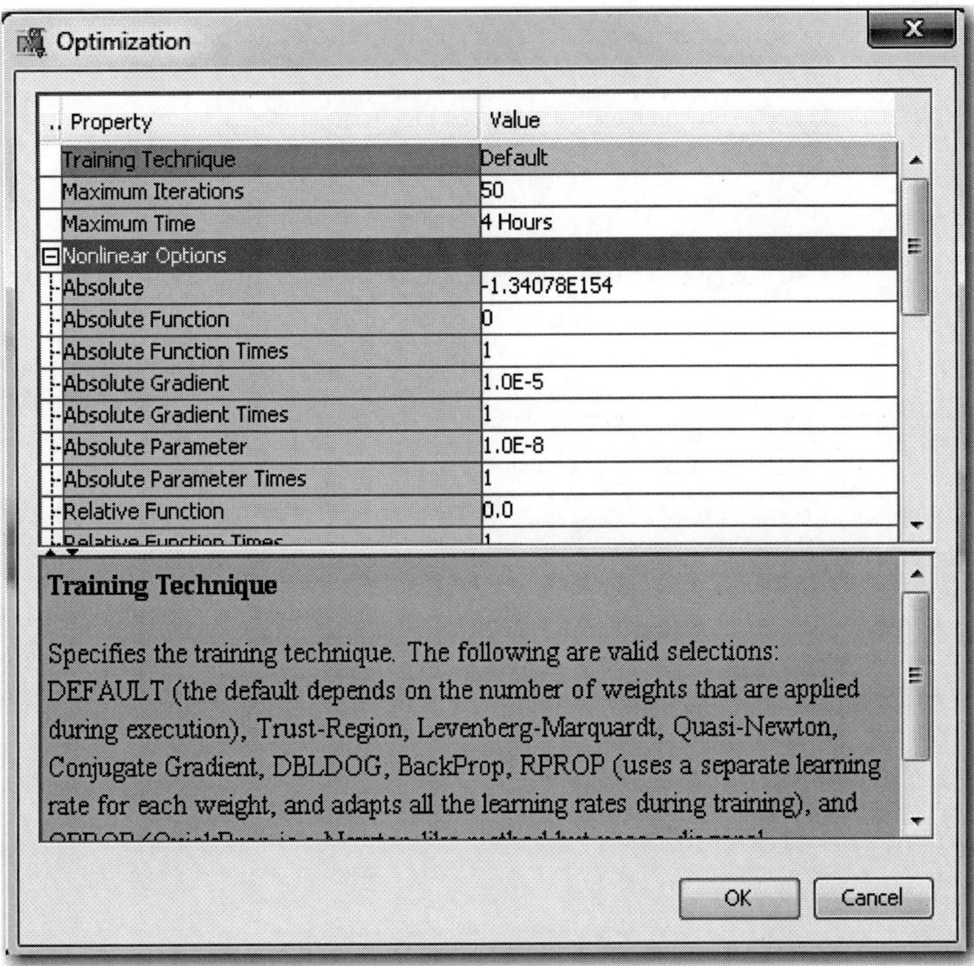

7. Scroll down and set Preliminary Training set **Enable** to No and select **OK**.

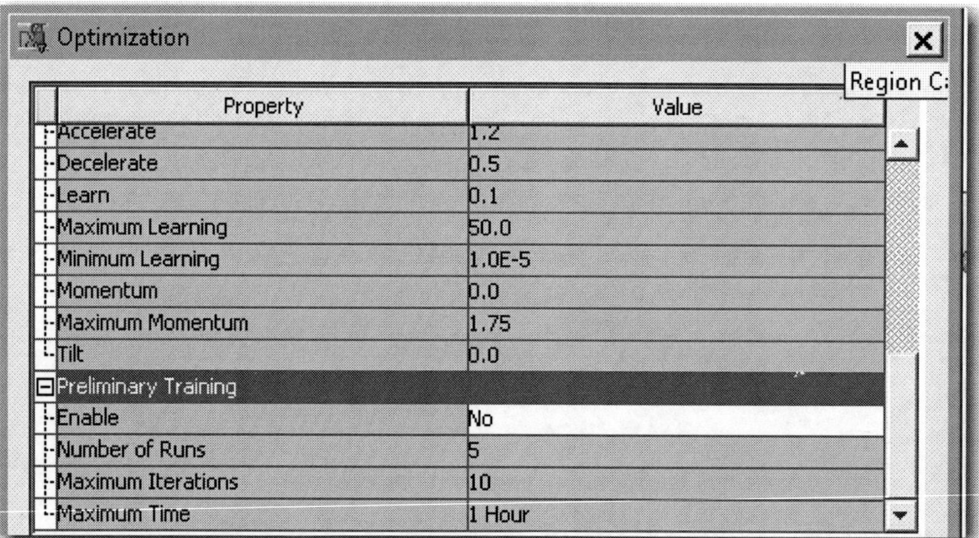

| Property | Value |
|---|---|
| Accelerate | 1.2 |
| Decelerate | 0.5 |
| Learn | 0.1 |
| Maximum Learning | 50.0 |
| Minimum Learning | 1.0E-5 |
| Momentum | 0.0 |
| Maximum Momentum | 1.75 |
| Tilt | 0.0 |
| Preliminary Training | |
| Enable | No |
| Number of Runs | 5 |
| Maximum Iterations | 10 |
| Maximum Time | 1 Hour |

8. Select [...] in the Network row of the Properties panel and examine the network options.

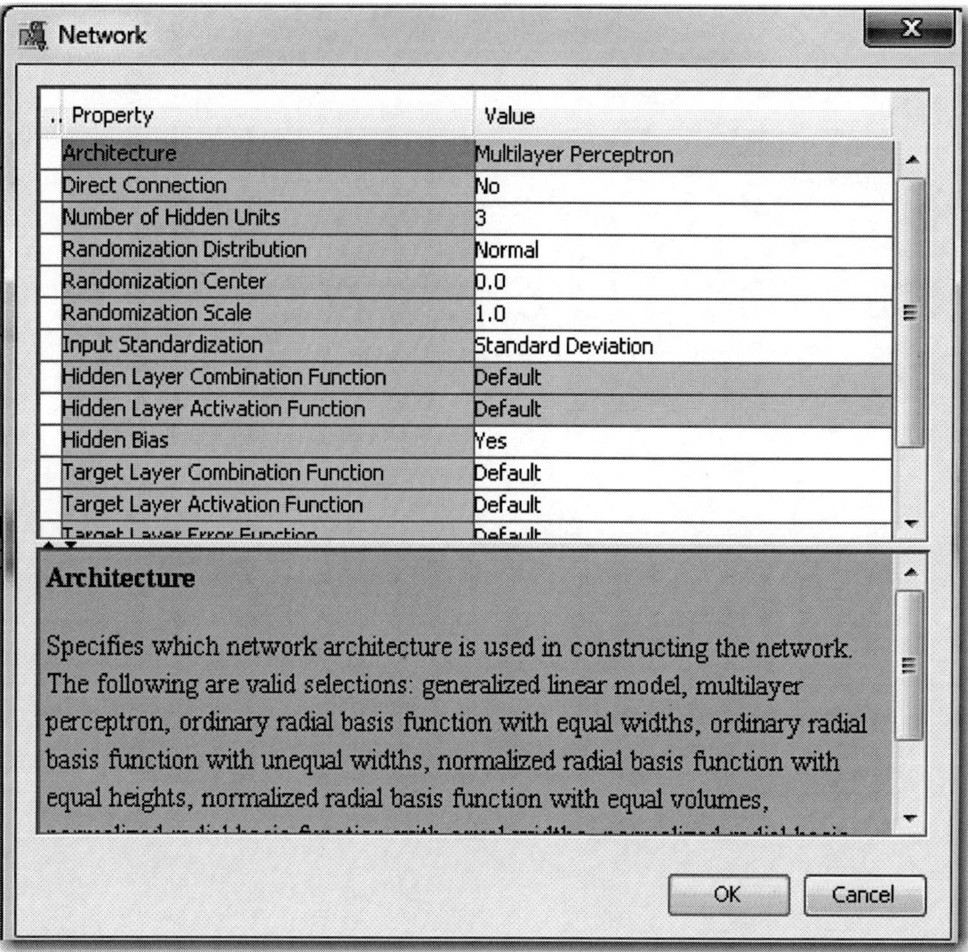

| Property | Value |
|---|---|
| Architecture | Multilayer Perceptron |
| Direct Connection | No |
| Number of Hidden Units | 3 |
| Randomization Distribution | Normal |
| Randomization Center | 0.0 |
| Randomization Scale | 1.0 |
| Input Standardization | Standard Deviation |
| Hidden Layer Combination Function | Default |
| Hidden Layer Activation Function | Default |
| Hidden Bias | Yes |
| Target Layer Combination Function | Default |
| Target Layer Activation Function | Default |

**Architecture**

Specifies which network architecture is used in constructing the network. The following are valid selections: generalized linear model, multilayer perceptron, ordinary radial basis function with equal widths, ordinary radial basis function with unequal widths, normalized radial basis function with equal heights, normalized radial basis function with equal volumes,

The Architecture property enables you to specify a wide variety of neural networks including

- generalized linear model (GLIM)
- multilayer perceptron (MLP, which is the default)
- ordinary radial basis function with equal widths (ORBFEQ)
- ordinary radial basis function with unequal widths (ORBFUN)
- normalized radial basis function with equal heights (NRBFEH)
- normalized radial basis function with equal volumes (NRBFEV)
- normalized radial basis function with equal widths (NRBFEW)
- normalized radial basis function with equal widths and heights (NRBFEQ)
- normalized radial basis function with unequal widths and heights (NRBFUN).

The User option in the field enables the user to define a network with a single hidden layer.

Discussion of these architectures is beyond the scope of this workshop.

By default, the network does not include direct connections. In this case, each input unit is connected to each hidden unit, and each hidden unit is connected to each output unit. If you set the Direct connections value to **Yes**, each input unit is also connected to each output unit. Direct connections define linear layers, whereas hidden neurons define nonlinear layers. Do not change the default setting for direct connections for this example.

The Number of Hidden Units property enables you to specify the number of hidden units that you want to use in each hidden layer. Permissible values are integers between 2 and 64. The default value is 3.

The remaining properties shown here enable you to specify the activation and combination functions used in the network. They also allow some specification of the distribution of the initial weights used in training and the use of bias terms in the model.

## Examining the Model

1. Run the flow from the Neural Network node and view the results.

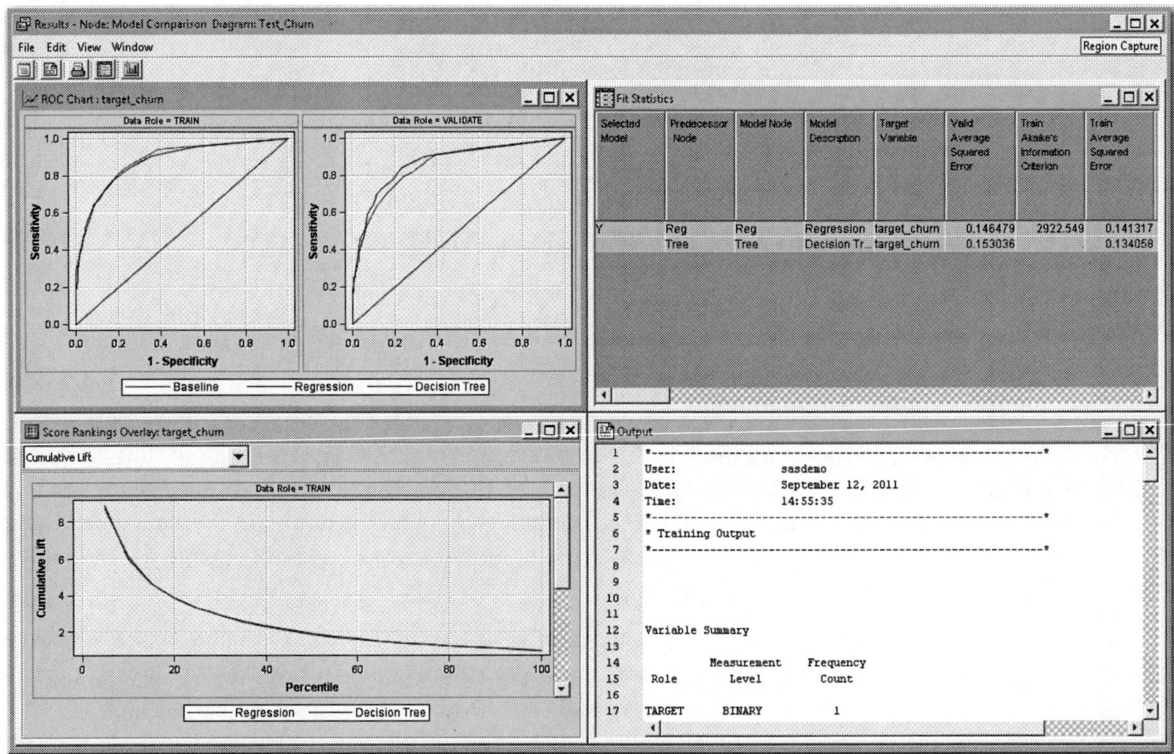


The Iteration Plot window shows that the final neural network chosen is from the 9th iteration. Recall that the model selection criterion was Average Square Error.

2. The Fit Statistics table shows that the validation Average Square Error is .141663.

Fit Statistics

| Target | Fit Statistics | Statistics Label | Train | Validation | Test |
|---|---|---|---|---|---|
| target_churn | _DFT_ | Total Degre... | 3294 | . | . |
| target_churn | _DFE_ | Degrees of ... | 3260 | . | . |
| target_churn | _DFM_ | Model Degr... | 34 | . | . |
| target_churn | _NW_ | Number of ... | 34 | . | . |
| target_churn | _AIC_ | Akaike's Inf... | 2872.889 | . | . |
| target_churn | _SBC_ | Schwarz's ... | 3080.285 | . | . |
| target_churn | _ASE_ | Average Sq... | 0.136701 | 0.140981 | . |
| target_churn | _MAX_ | Maximum A... | 0.993276 | 0.982855 | . |
| target_churn | _DIV_ | Divisor for A... | 6588 | 2828 | . |
| target_churn | _NOBS_ | Sum of Fre... | 3294 | 1414 | . |
| target_churn | _RASE_ | Root Avera... | 0.369731 | 0.375474 | . |
| target_churn | _SSE_ | Sum of Squ... | 900.585 | 398.6939 | . |
| target_churn | _SUMW_ | Sum of Cas... | 6588 | 2828 | . |
| target_churn | _FPE_ | Final Predic... | 0.139552 | . | . |
| target_churn | _MSE_ | Mean Squa... | 0.138127 | 0.140981 | . |
| target_churn | _RFPE_ | Root Final ... | 0.373567 | . | . |
| target_churn | _RMSE_ | Root Mean ... | 0.371654 | 0.375474 | . |
| target_churn | _AVERR_ | Average Err... | 0.425757 | 0.440727 | . |
| target_churn | _ERR_ | Error Functi... | 2804.889 | 1246.375 | . |
| target_churn | _MISC_ | Misclassific... | 0.372192 | 0.378359 | . |
| target_churn | _WRONG_ | Number of ... | 1226 | 535 | . |
| target_churn | _PROF_ | Total Profit f... | 5325.486 | 2255.995 | . |
| target_churn | _APROF_ | Average Pr... | 1.616723 | 1.59547 | |

## Examining Results from the Model Comparison Node

1. Now run the **Model Comparison** node and view the results.
2. **Model Comparison** node results.

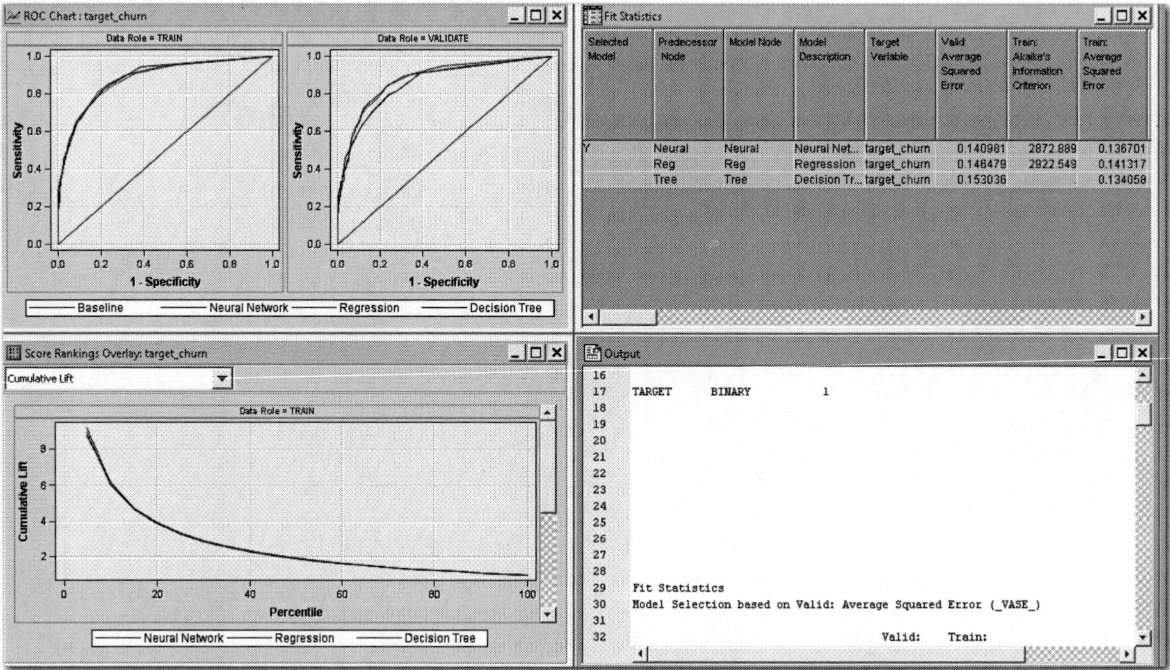


3. Maximize the Output window and examine the report and examine the Fit Statistics report. We see that the Neural Network model was chosen based on average square error on the validation data.

Fit Statistics
Model Selection based on Valid: Average Squared Error (_VASE_)

| Selected Model | Model Node | Model Description | Valid: Average Squared Error | Train: Average Squared Error | Train: Misclassification Rate | Valid: Misclassification Rate |
|---|---|---|---|---|---|---|
| Y | Neural | Neural Network | 0.14098 | 0.13670 | 0.37219 | 0.37836 |
| | Reg | Regression | 0.14648 | 0.14132 | 0.38130 | 0.37977 |
| | Tree | Decision Tree | 0.15304 | 0.13406 | 0.37432 | 0.38967 |

The ROC chart also indicates that the neural network model performs the best of the three models.

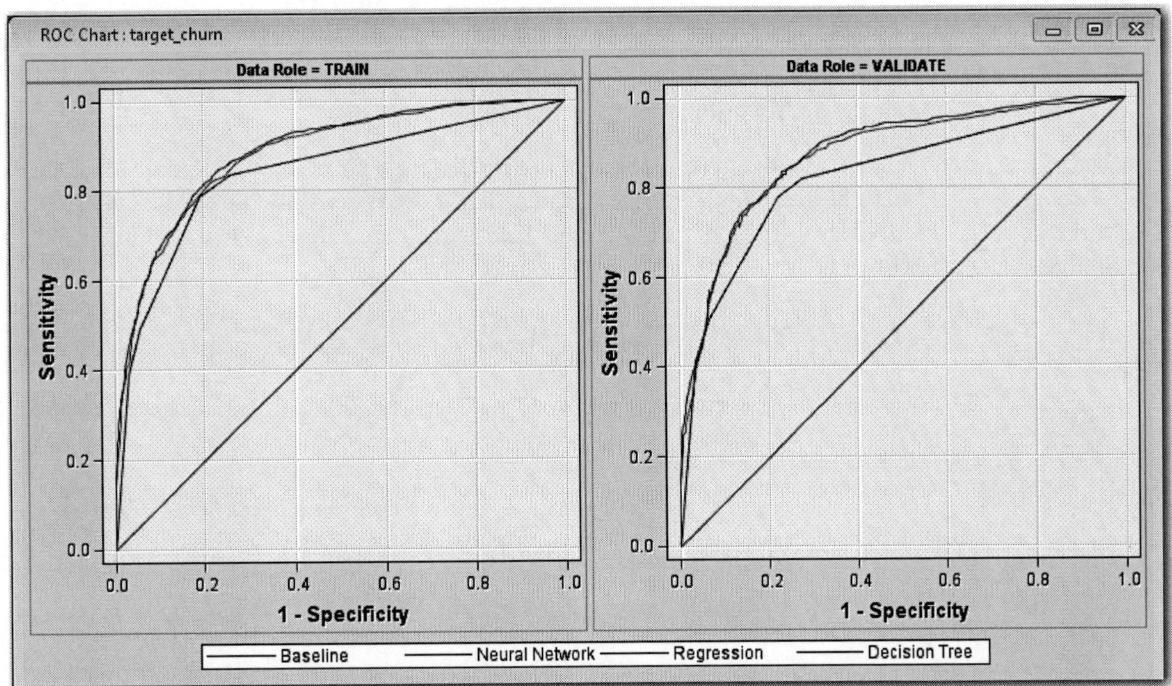

## Scoring New Data

1. The next step in this process is to score customers using this model or one of the other models. The flow below shows the Regression Node scoring the scoring table, Churn_RPM_Score. Note when this table is created in Enterprise Miner the role must be **Score**.

   Now we can score customers to determine if they are predicted to churn by the model we chose to use for scoring. The data to be scored in the table, **Churn_RPM_Score**, will be linked to Enterprise Miner as we did with Churn_RPM. This table must be assigned the role of **Score** in step 7 of the Data Source Wizard as shown below.

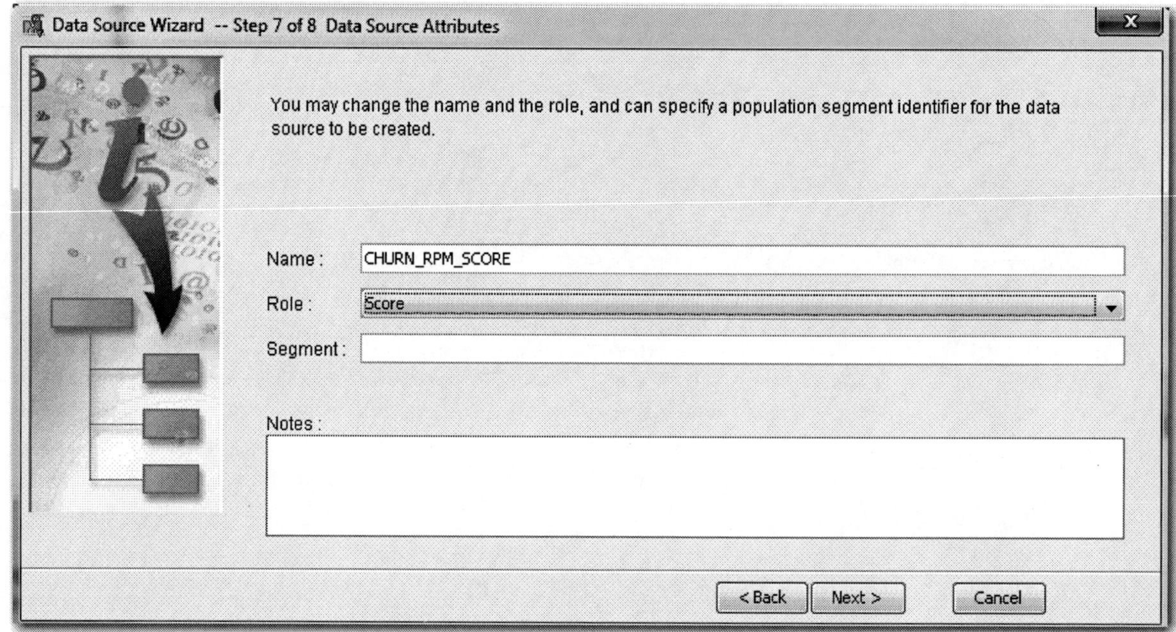

2. We decide to use the regression model to score this table, see the diagram below for how the **Score Node**, **Regression** node, and **Churn_Rpm_Score** are connected.

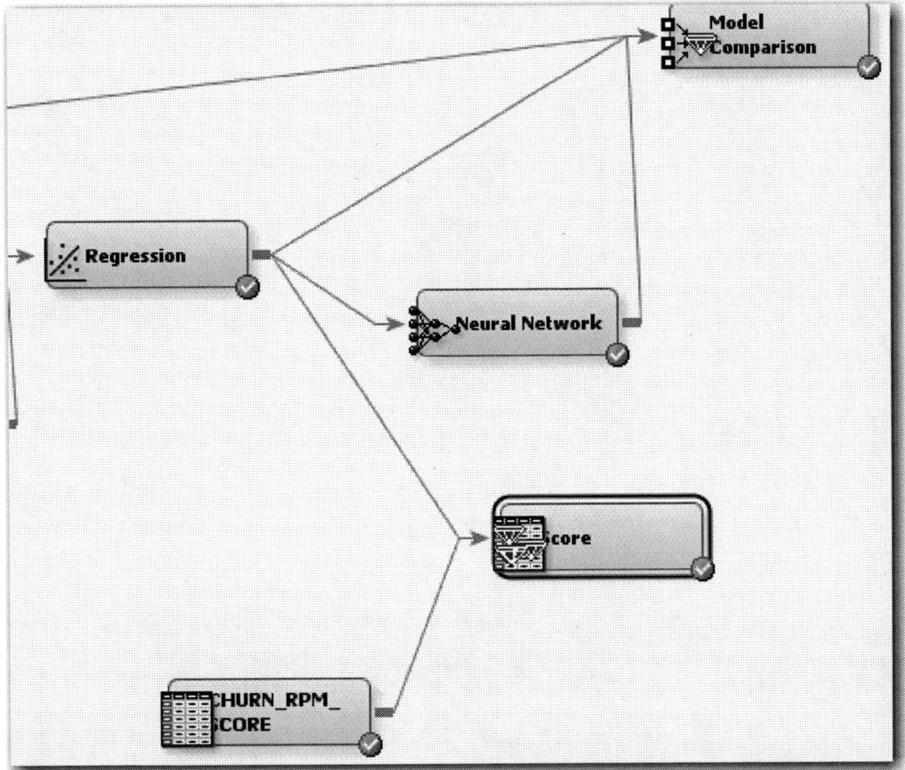


3. The results of the **Score** node show the scoring code and the variables in the output data table.

Optimized SAS Code

```
*------------------------------------------------------------*;
* EM SCORE CODE;
* VERSION: 6.2;
* GENERATED BY: toboha;
* CREATED: 10MAY2011:19:38:57;
*------------------------------------------------------------*;
*------------------------------------------------------------*;
* TOOL: Input Data Source;
* TYPE: SAMPLE;
* NODE: Ids;
*------------------------------------------------------------*;
*------------------------------------------------------------*;
* TOOL: Partition Class;
* TYPE: SAMPLE;
* NODE: Part;
*------------------------------------------------------------*;
*------------------------------------------------------------*;
* TOOL: Transform;
* TYPE: MODIFY;
* NODE: Trans;
*------------------------------------------------------------*;
drop _SCALEVAR_;
if current_billamount ne . then _SCALEVAR_ = max((current_billamount - -690), 0.0)/(325127 - -690);
else _SCALEVAR_ = .;
LOG_current_billamount = log(_SCALEVAR_ + 1);
```

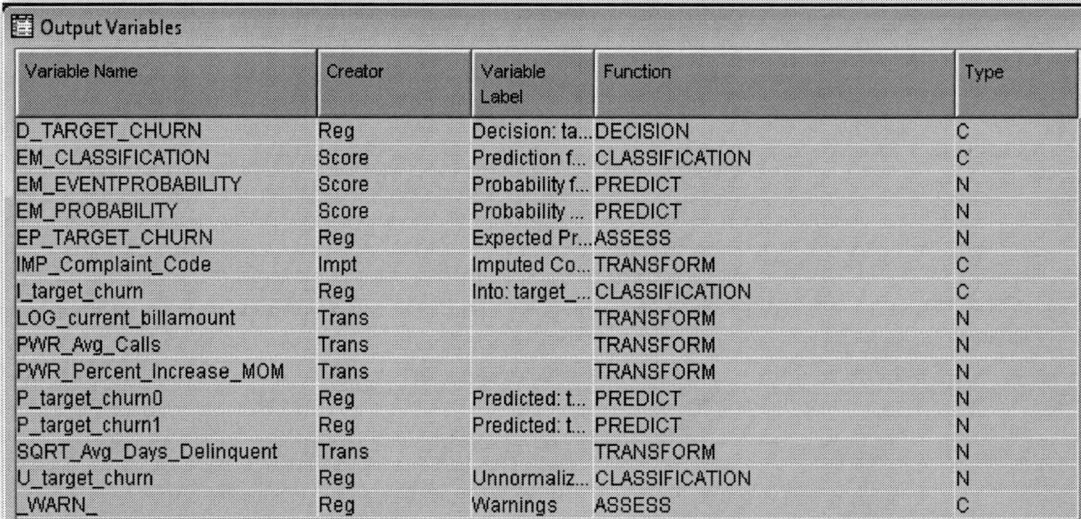

Output Variables

| Variable Name | Creator | Variable Label | Function | Type |
|---|---|---|---|---|
| D_TARGET_CHURN | Reg | Decision: ta... | DECISION | C |
| EM_CLASSIFICATION | Score | Prediction f... | CLASSIFICATION | C |
| EM_EVENTPROBABILITY | Score | Probability f... | PREDICT | N |
| EM_PROBABILITY | Score | Probability ... | PREDICT | N |
| EP_TARGET_CHURN | Reg | Expected Pr... | ASSESS | N |
| IMP_Complaint_Code | Impt | Imputed Co... | TRANSFORM | C |
| I_target_churn | Reg | Into: target_... | CLASSIFICATION | C |
| LOG_current_billamount | Trans | | TRANSFORM | N |
| PWR_Avg_Calls | Trans | | TRANSFORM | N |
| PWR_Percent_Increase_MOM | Trans | | TRANSFORM | N |
| P_target_churn0 | Reg | Predicted: t... | PREDICT | N |
| P_target_churn1 | Reg | Predicted: t... | PREDICT | N |
| SQRT_Avg_Days_Delinquent | Trans | | TRANSFORM | N |
| U_target_churn | Reg | Unnormaliz... | CLASSIFICATION | N |
| _WARN_ | Reg | Warnings | ASSESS | C |

Note in the table is a classification variables, which identifies those customers predicted by the model to churn. This information can be used by marketing or customer service to try and retain those churners which are good customers.

4. We can now go to the output table from the **Score** node and identify the churners.

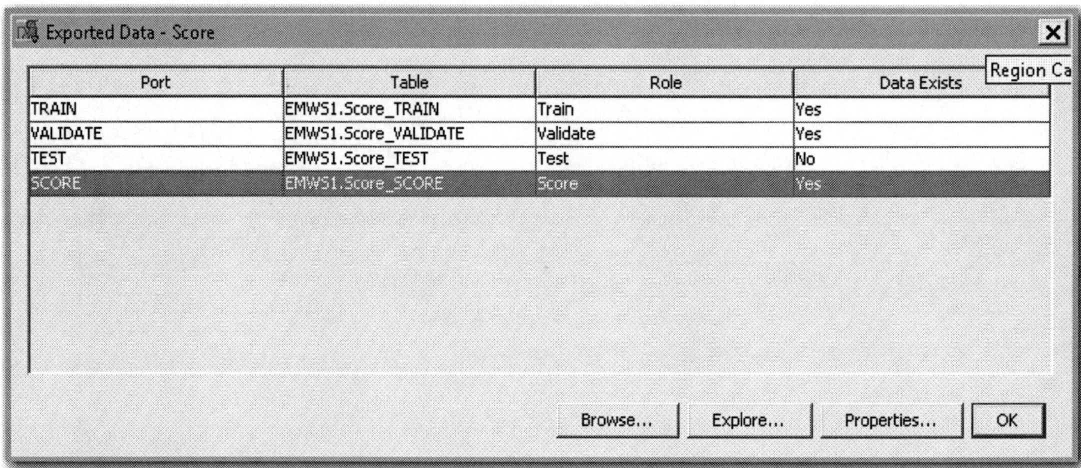

Exported Data - Score

| Port | Table | Role | Data Exists |
|---|---|---|---|
| TRAIN | EMWS1.Score_TRAIN | Train | Yes |
| VALIDATE | EMWS1.Score_VALIDATE | Validate | Yes |
| TEST | EMWS1.Score_TEST | Test | No |
| SCORE | EMWS1.Score_SCORE | Score | Yes |



5. Select **Browse** and examine the table.

EMWS1.Score_SCORE

| | Predicted: target_churn=0 | Probability for level 1 of target_churn | Probability of Classification | Prediction for Region Capture |
|---|---|---|---|---|
| 1 | 0.9858651973592611 | 0.014134802640738861 | 0.9858651973592611 | 0 |
| 2 | 0.9968102625167451 | 0.0031897374832549237 | 0.9968102625167451 | 0 |
| 3 | 0.9828935883080422 | 0.017106411691957903 | 0.9828935883080422 | 0 |
| 4 | 0.3758028732313823 | 0.6241971267686178 | 0.6241971267686178 | 1 |
| 5 | 0.9278604754065698 | 0.07213952459343015 | 0.9278604754065698 | 0 |
| 6 | 0.9990236992446194 | 9.763007553805401E-4 | 0.9990236992446194 | 0 |
| 7 | 0.9777449245253194 | 0.022255075474680697 | 0.9777449245253194 | 0 |
| 8 | 0.979927737091652 | 0.02007226290834798 | 0.979927737091652 | 0 |
| 9 | 0.4935722364964327 | 0.5064277635035673 | 0.5064277635035673 | 1 |
| 10 | 0.9950341028724158 | 0.004965897127584212 | 0.9950341028724158 | 0 |
| 11 | 0.9944939811973535 | 0.005506018802646391 | 0.9944939811973535 | 0 |
| 12 | 0.9920545074584131 | 0.007945492541586847 | 0.9920545074584131 | 0 |
| 13 | 0.882585240695465 | 0.11741475930453497 | 0.882585240695465 | 0 |
| 14 | 0.981507248392501 | 0.01849275160749903 | 0.981507248392501 | 0 |
| 15 | 0.9751235334966313 | 0.024876466503368708 | 0.9751235334966313 | 0 |
| 16 | 0.9631553913117578 | 0.03684460868824218 | 0.9631553913117578 | 0 |
| 17 | 0.9813299525459992 | 0.01867004745400089 | 0.9813299525459992 | 0 |
| 18 | 0.9896872249475756 | 0.010312775052424504 | 0.9896872249475756 | 0 |

# Exercises

## 1. Initial Data Exploration

A supermarket is offering a new line of organic products. The supermarket's management wants to determine which customers are likely to purchase these products.

The supermarket has a customer loyalty program. As an initial buyer incentive plan, the supermarket provided coupons for the organic products to all of their loyalty program participants and collected data that includes whether or not these customers purchased any of the organic products.

The **ORGANICS** data set contains 13 variables and over 22,000 observations. The variables in the data set are shown below with the appropriate roles and levels.

| Name | Model Role | Measurement Level | Description |
|---|---|---|---|
| **ID** | ID | Nominal | Customer loyalty identification number |
| **DEMAFFL** | Input | Interval | Affluence grade on a scale from 1 to 30 |
| **DEMAGE** | Input | Interval | Age, in years |
| **DEMCLUSTER** | Rejected | Nominal | Type of residential neighborhood |
| **DEMCLUSTERGROUP** | Input | Nominal | Neighborhood group |
| **DEMGENDER** | Input | Nominal | M = male, F = female, U = unknown |
| **DEMREGION** | Input | Nominal | Geographic region |
| **DEMTVREG** | Input | Nominal | Television region |
| **PROMCLASS** | Input | Nominal | Loyalty status: tin, silver, gold, or platinum |
| **PROMSPEND** | Input | Interval | Total amount spent |
| **PROMTIME** | Input | Interval | Time as loyalty card member |
| **TARGETBUY** | Target | Binary | Organics purchased? 1 = Yes, 0 = No |
| **TARGETAMT** | Rejected | Interval | Number of organic products purchased |

Although two target variables are listed, these exercises concentrate on the binary variable **TARGETBUY**.

**a.** Create a new project named Exercises and a diagram named Organics.

**b.** Define the data set **GARPM.ORGANICS** as a data source for the project.

- Set the roles for the analysis variables as shown above.
- Examine the distribution of the target variable. What is the proportion of individuals who purchased organic products?

  **Answer:** 7,566 / 22,223

1) The variable **DEMCLUSTERGROUP** contains collapsed levels of the variable **DEMCLUSTER**. Presume that, based on previous experience; you believe that **DEMCLUSTERGROUP** is sufficient for this type of modeling effort. Set the model role for **DEMCLUSTER** to **Rejected**.

2) As noted above, only **TARGETBUY** will be used for this analysis and should have a role of **Rejected**. Can **TARGETAMT** be used as an input for a model used to predict **TARGETBUY**? Why or why not?

   **Answer:** no

3) Finish the **Organics** data source definition.

**c.** Add the **GARPM.ORGANICS** data source to the Organics diagram workspace.

**d.** Add a Data Partition node to the diagram and connect it to the Data Source node. Assign 50% of the data for training and 50% for validation.

**e.** Add a Decision Tree node to the workspace and connect it to the Data Partition node.

**f.** Create a decision tree model interactively, automatically, or autonomously using average squared error as the model assessment statistic.

1) Create the tree.

2) How many leaves are in the optimal tree?

   **Answer:** ____________________

3) Which variable was used for the first split? What were the competing splits for this first split?

   **Answer:** ____________________

2. **Predictive Modeling Using Regression**

   a. Return to the Organics diagram in the Exercises project. Use the StatExplore tool on the **ORGANICS** data source.

   b. In preparation for regression, is any missing values imputation needed? If yes, should you do this imputation before generating the decision tree models? Why or why not?

   c. Add an Impute node to the diagram and connect it to the Data Partition node. Set the node to impute "U" for unknown class variable values, the overall mean for unknown interval variable values, and create imputation indicators for all imputed inputs.

   d. Add a Regression node to the diagram and connect it to the Impute node.

   e. Choose the stepwise selection and average squared error as the selection criterion.

   f. Run the Regression node and view the results. Which variables are included in the final model? Which variables are important in this model? What is the validation ASE?

   g. In preparation for regression, are any transformations of the data warranted? Why or why not?

   h. Disconnect the Impute node from the Data Partition node. Add a Transform Variables node to the diagram and connect it to the Data Partition node. Connect the Transform Variables node to the Impute node.

   i. Apply a log transformation to the **DemAffl**, **PromSpend**, and **PromTime** inputs.

   j. Run the Transform Variables node. Explore the exported training data. Did the transformations result in less skewed distributions?

   k. Rerun the Regression node. Do the selected variables change? How about the validation ASE?

   l. Create a full second-degree polynomial model. How does the validation average squared error for the polynomial model compare to the original model?

3. **Predictive Modeling Using Neural Networks**

   a. In preparation for a neural network model, is imputation of missing values needed? Why or why not?

   b. In preparation for a neural network model, is data transformation generally needed? Why or why not?

   c. Add a Neural Network tool to the Organics diagram. Connect the Impute node to the Neural Network node.

   d. Set the model selection criterion to average squared error.

   e. Run the Neural Network node and examine the validation average squared error. How does it compare to other models?

4. **Scoring Organics Data**

   a. Create a Score data source for the **ScoreOrganics** data.

   b. Score the **ScoreOrganics** data using the model selected with the Model Comparison node.

# 1.6 Solutions

## Solutions to Exercises

1. **Initial Data Exploration**

   a. After creating a new project named Exercises, create a new diagram named Organics.

      1) Select **File** ⇨ **New** ⇨ **Diagram…**. The Create New Diagram window opens.

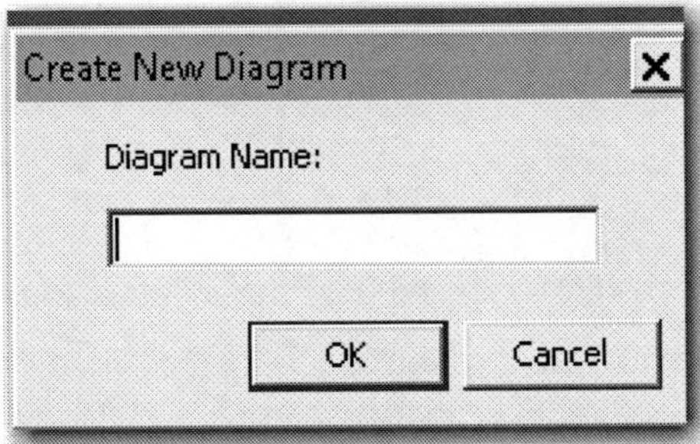


      2) Type **Organics** in the **Diagram Name** field.

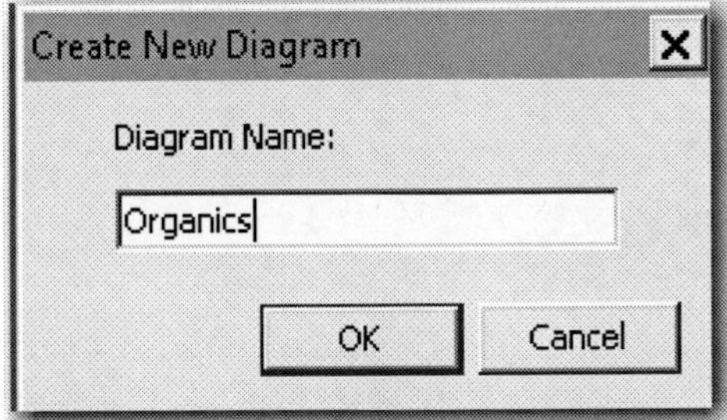


      3) Select **OK**

   b. Define the data set **GARPM.ORGANICS** as a data source for the project.

      1) Select **File** ⇨ **New** ⇨ **Library…**. The Library Wizard window opens.

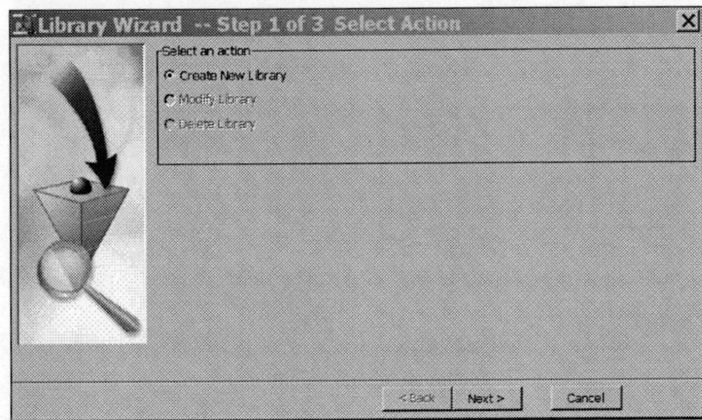


      2) Select **Next**

3) Type **GARPM** in the **Name** field. In the **Path** field, type **C:\Workshop\Winsas\Garpm\data**.

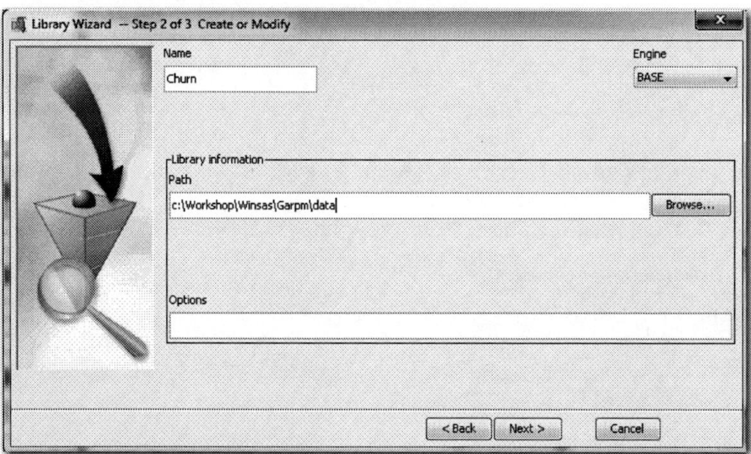


4) Select **Next**. The wizard proceeds to Step 3 and indicates that the library was created.

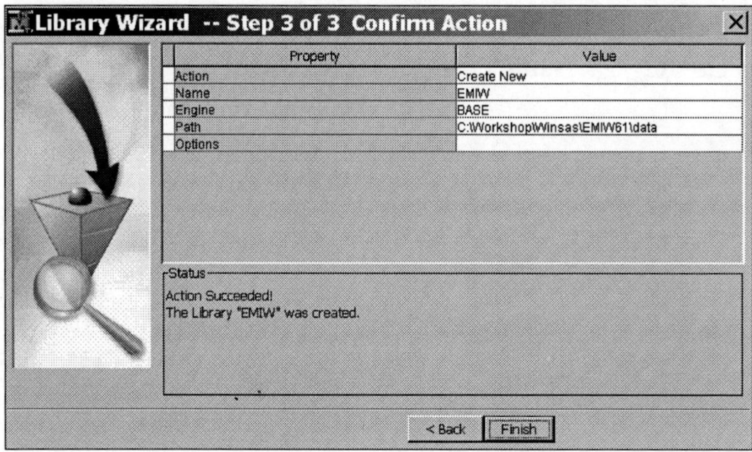


5) Now define the data source for SAS Enterprise Miner. Select **File** ⇨ **New** ⇨ **Data Source…**.

6) Type **GARPM.ORGANICS** in the **Table** field or browse to find this table.

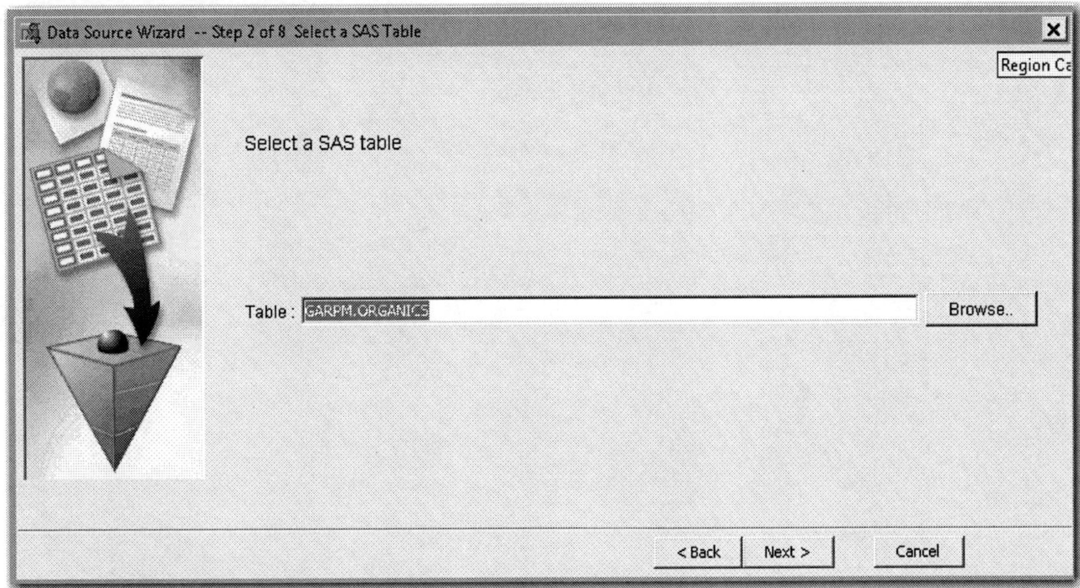


7) Select Next > The wizard proceeds to step 3.

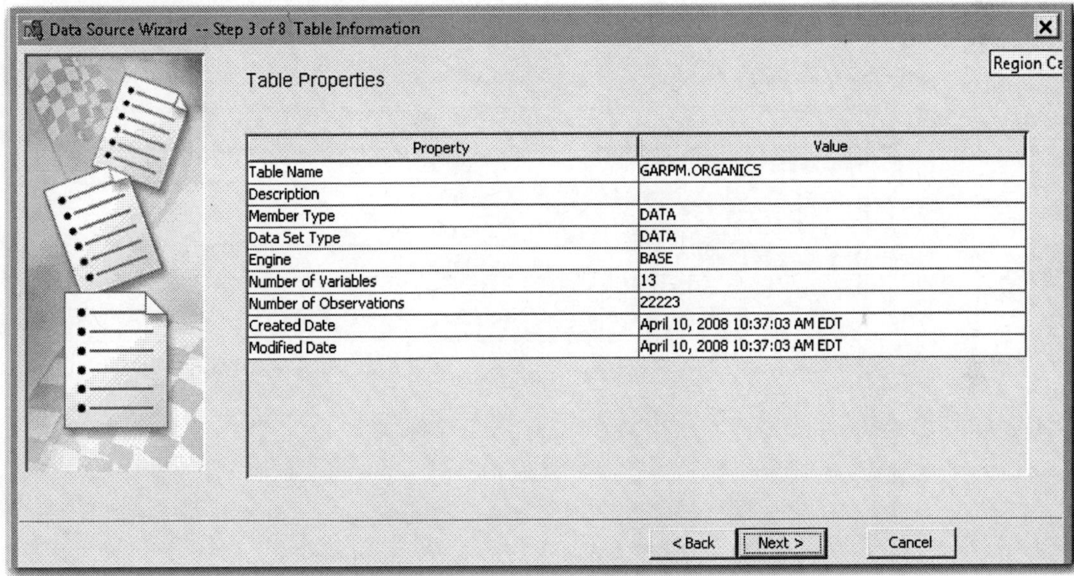

8) Select **Next >**. The wizard proceeds to step 4.

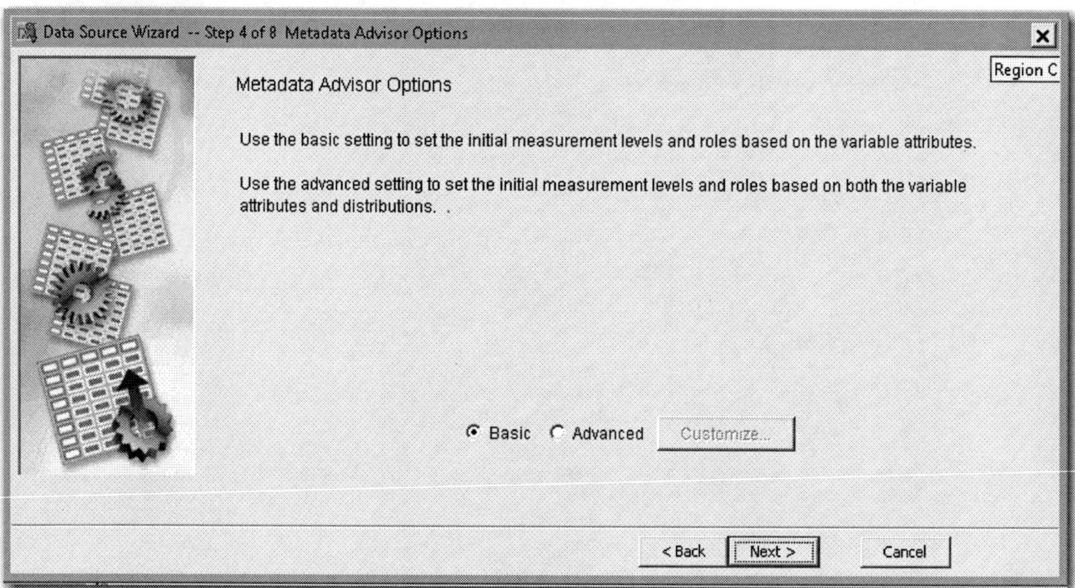


9) Select the **Advanced** button and select **Customize**. The Advanced Advisor Options window opens.

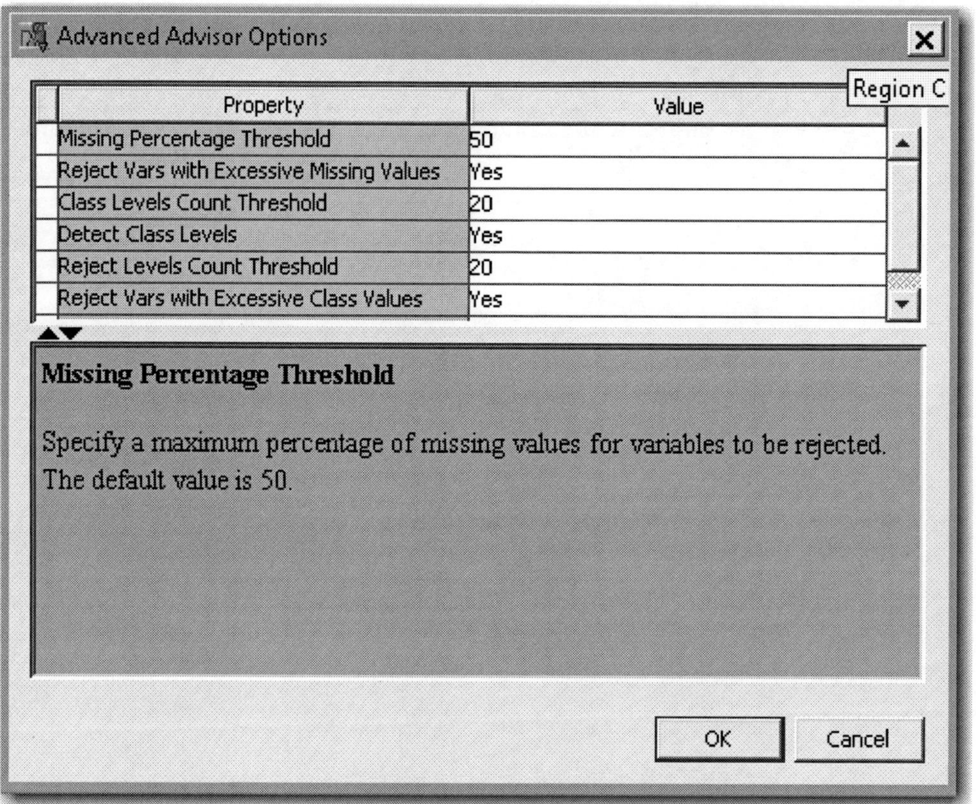

10) Type **2** in the **Class Levels Count Threshold** field, which gives you only binary nominal variables.

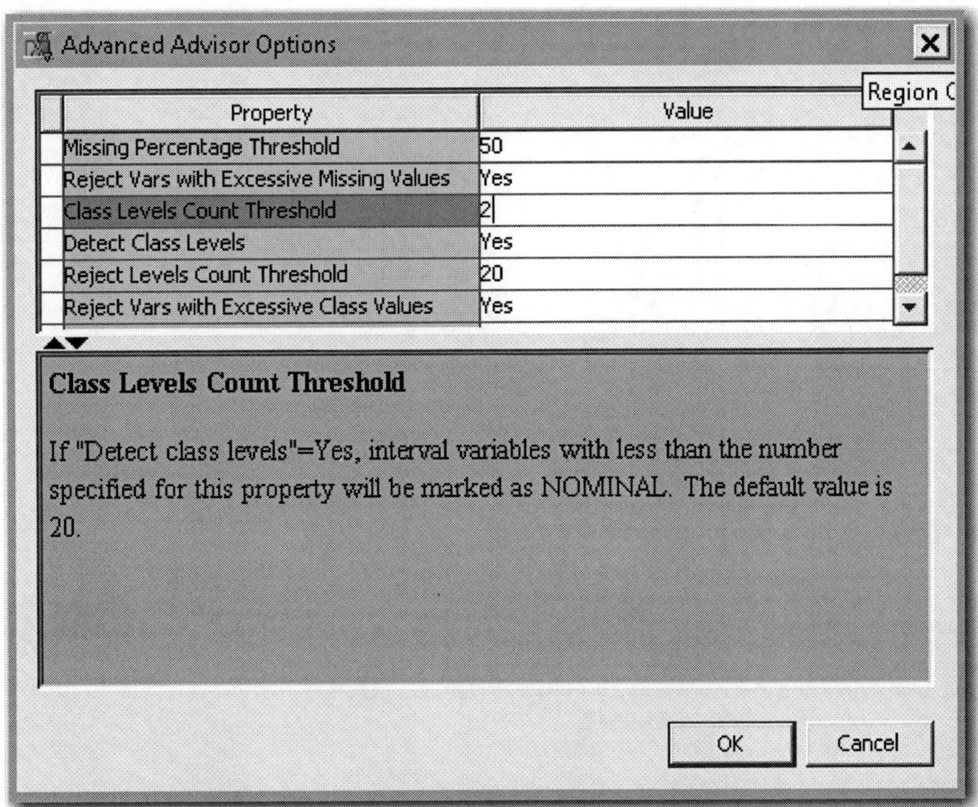


11) Select OK. The Advanced Advisor Options window closes, and you return to step 4 of the Data Source Wizard.

12) Select Next >. The wizard proceeds to step 5.

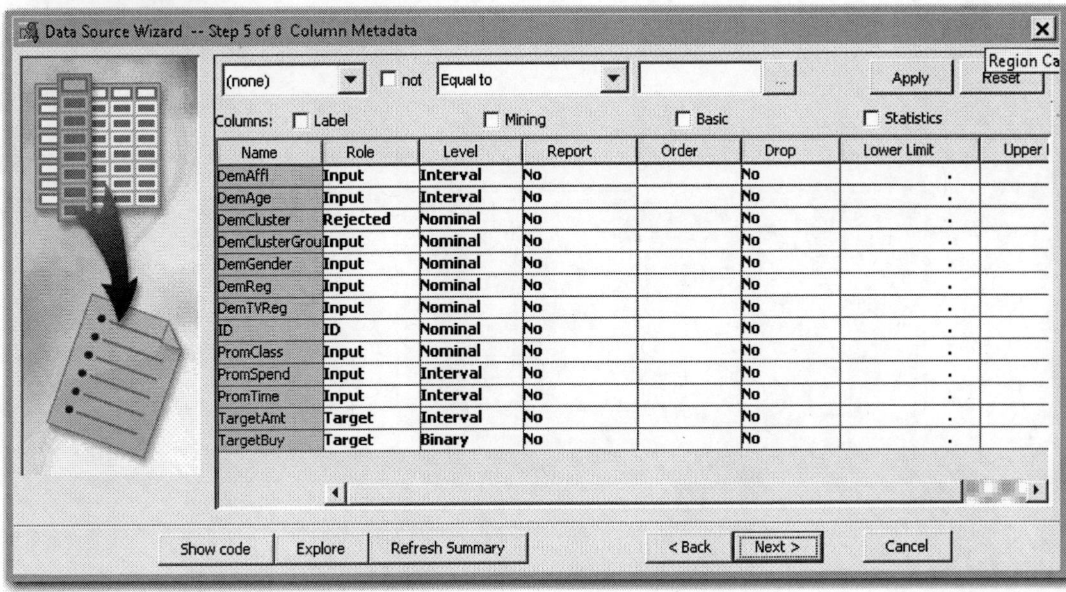

Note that by customizing the Advanced Metadata Advisor, most of the roles and levels are correctly set.

13) Select **Role** ⇨ **Rejected** for **TargetAmt**.

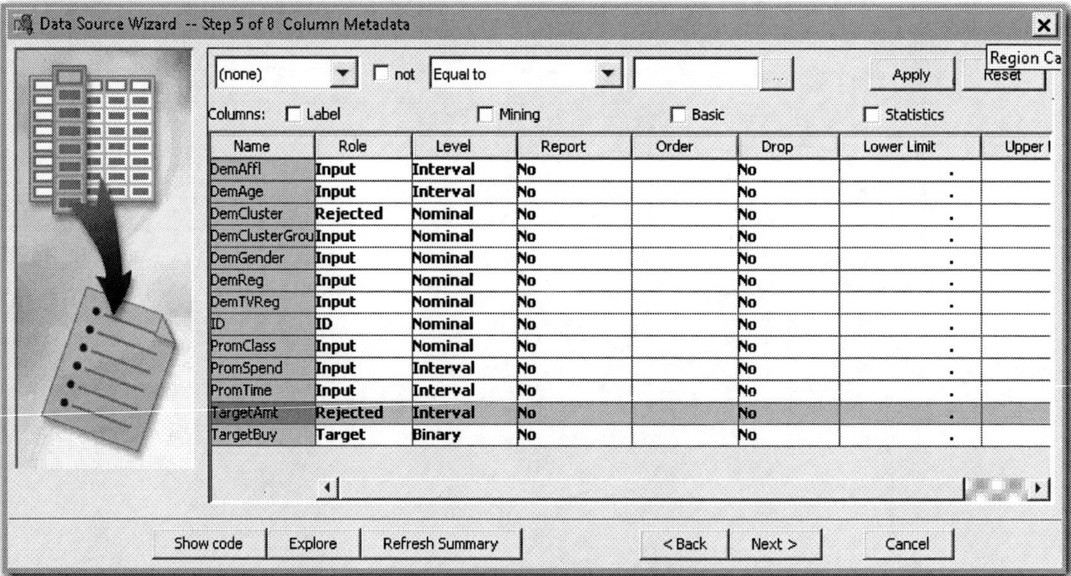

Examine the distribution of the target variable. **What is the proportion of individuals who purchased organic products?**

14) Select the **TargetBuy** row and select Explore... . The Explore window opens.

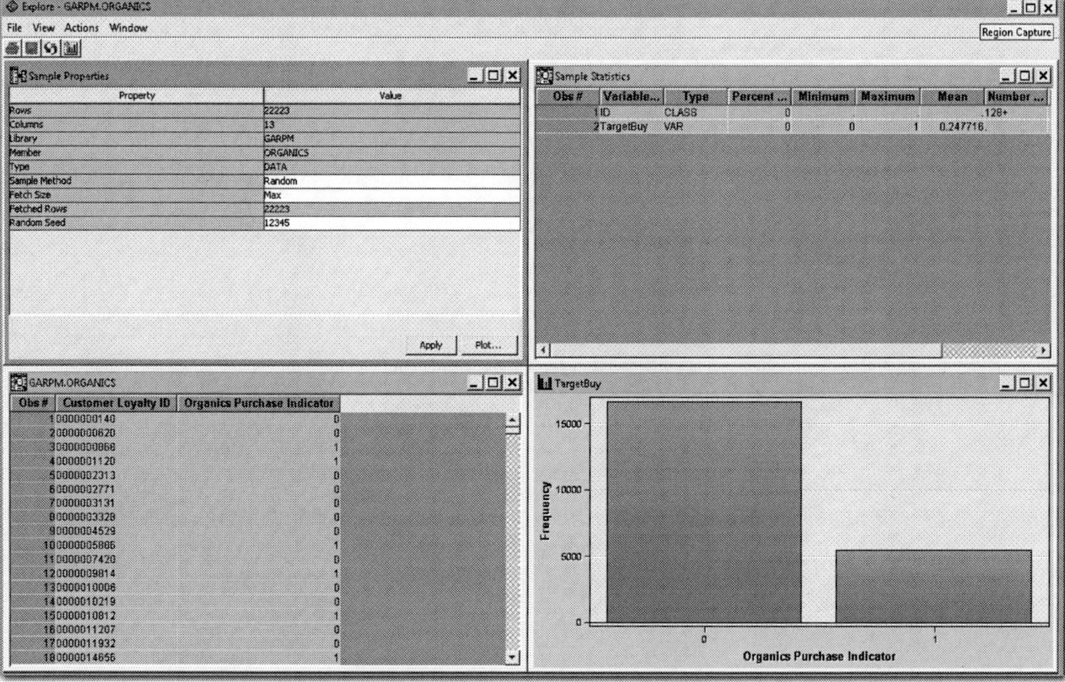

The proportion of individuals who purchased organic products appears to be 25%. To change from frequency to percentages, right-click in the chart area and select **Data Options**. For the **Response statistic** field, select **Percent**, as shown in the window below.

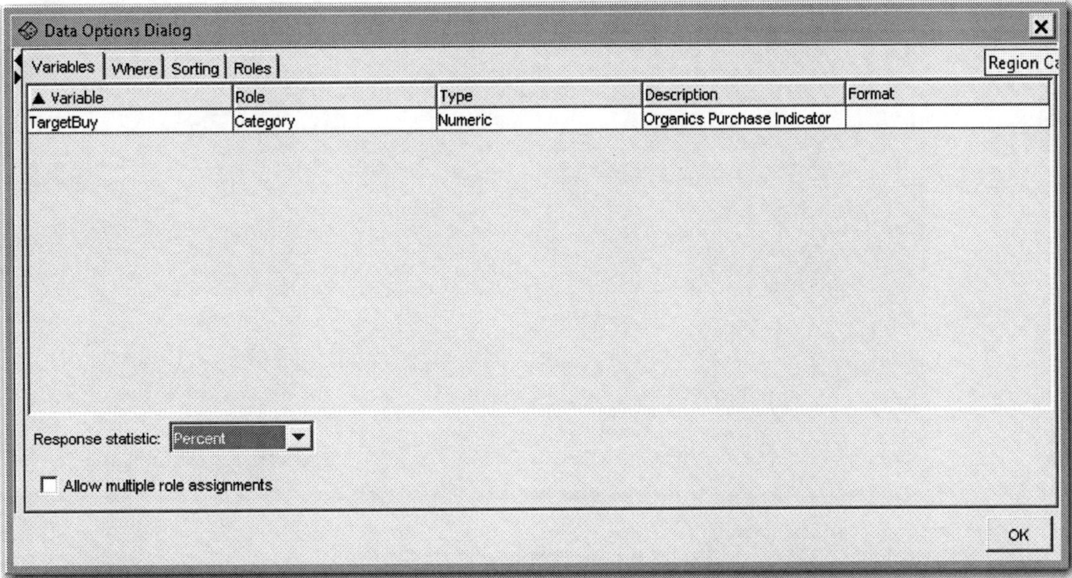


15) Select OK and place the cursor on the bar corresponding to 1. Observe that the percent is 24.777%.

16) Close the Explore window.

17) The variable **DemClusterGroup** contains collapsed levels of the variable **DemCluster**. Presume that, based on previous experience; you believe that **DemClusterGroup** is sufficient for this type of modeling effort. Set the model role for **DemCluster** to **Rejected**.

18) This is already done, using the Advanced Metadata Advisor. Otherwise, select **Role** ⇨ **Rejected** for **DemCluster**.

19) As noted above, only **TargetBuy** will be used for this analysis and should have a role of Target. **Can TargetAmt be used as an input for a model used to predict TargetBuy? Why or why not?**

No, using **TargetAmt** as an input is not possible. It is measured at the same time as **TargetBuy** and is used to define the target variable.

20) Finish the Organics data source definition. Select Next >. The wizard proceeds to step 6.

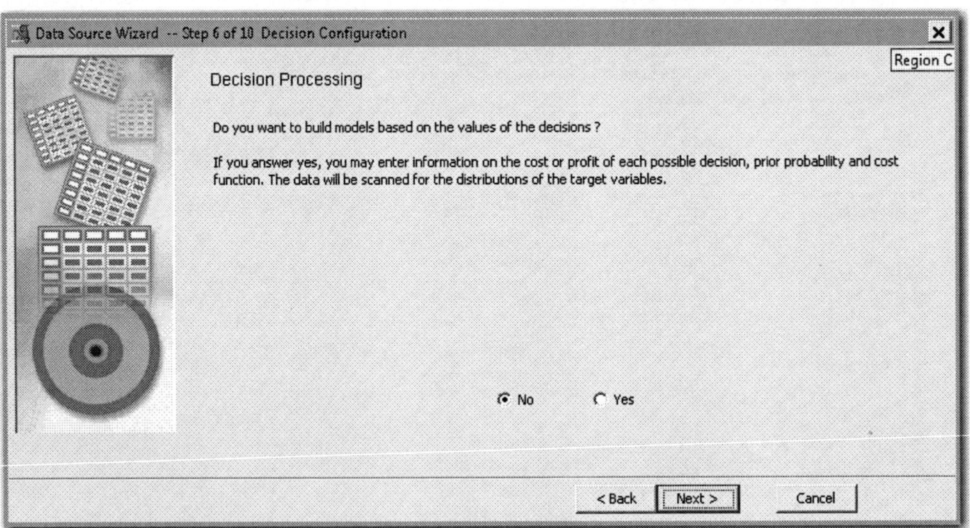


21) Select Next >. The wizard proceeds to step 7.

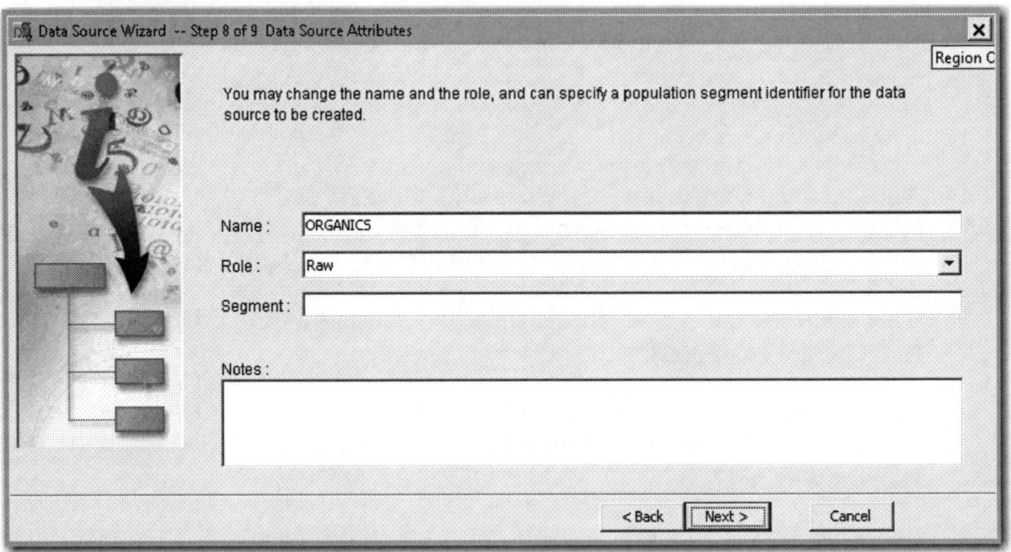


Note that the role of the data source is Raw.

22) Select Next >. A summary of the metadata is presented.

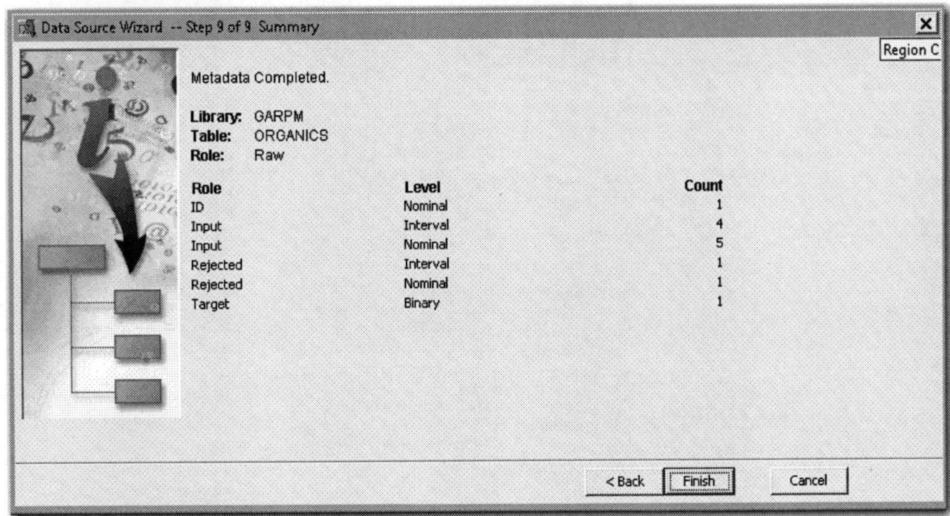


23) Select Finish. The wizard closes, and the **Organics** data source is ready for use in the Project panel.

c. Add the **GARPM.ORGANICS** data source to the Organics diagram workspace.

**d.** Add a **Data Partition** node to the diagram and connect it to the Data Source node. Assign 50% of the data for training and 50% for validation.

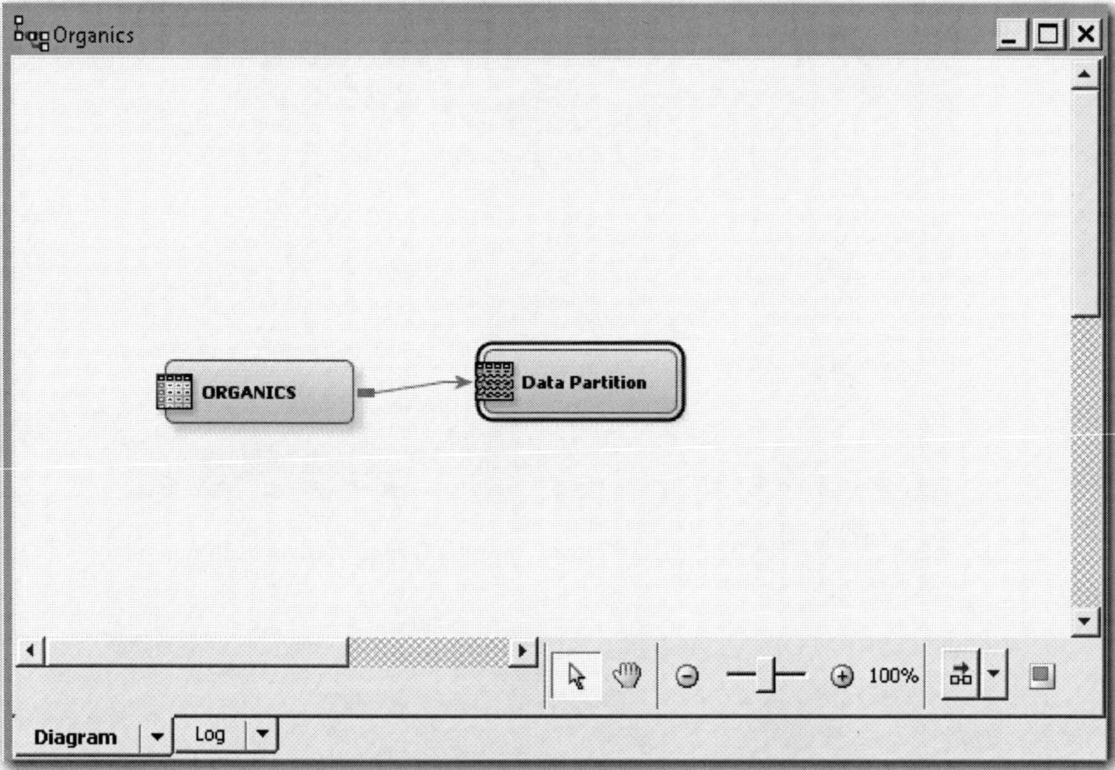


1) Type **50** in the **Training** and **Validation** fields under Data Set Allocations.

2) Type **0** in the **Test** field.

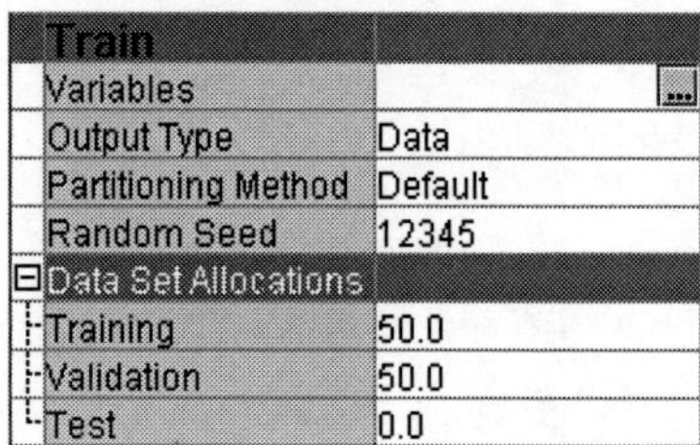

| Train | |
|---|---|
| Variables | ... |
| Output Type | Data |
| Partitioning Method | Default |
| Random Seed | 12345 |
| Data Set Allocations | |
| Training | 50.0 |
| Validation | 50.0 |
| Test | 0.0 |

e. Add a **Decision Tree** node to the workspace and connect it to the **Data Partition** node.

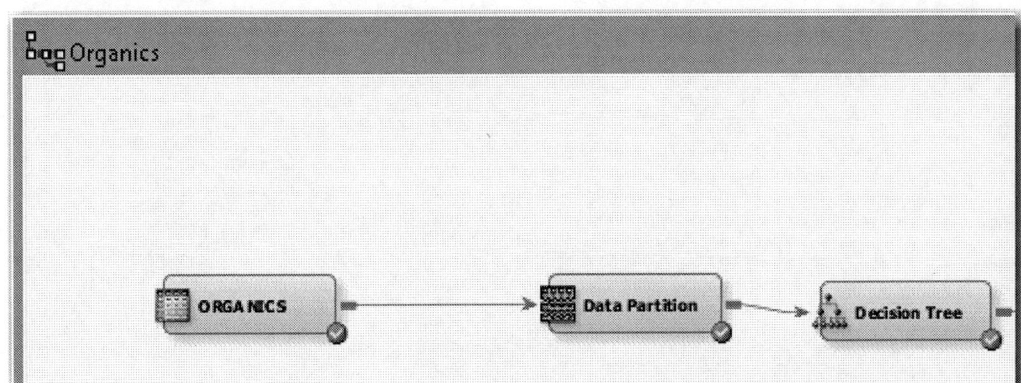


f. Create a decision tree model interactively, automatically, or autonomously using average squared error as the model assessment statistic. **In this solution, the tree is created autonomously.**

1) Select **Average Square Error** for the Assessment Measure property.

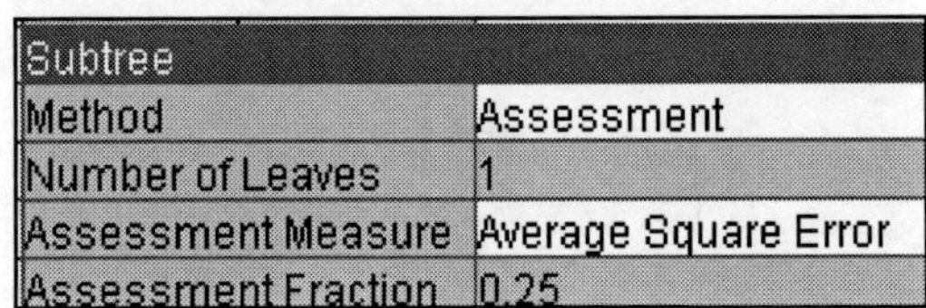

| Subtree | |
|---|---|
| Method | Assessment |
| Number of Leaves | 1 |
| Assessment Measure | Average Square Error |
| Assessment Fraction | 0.25 |

2) Right-click on the **Decision Tree** node and select **Run** from the option menu.

3) Select Yes in the Confirmation window.

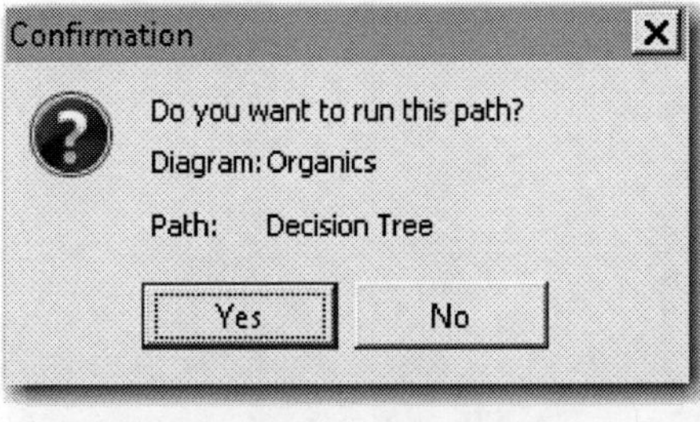


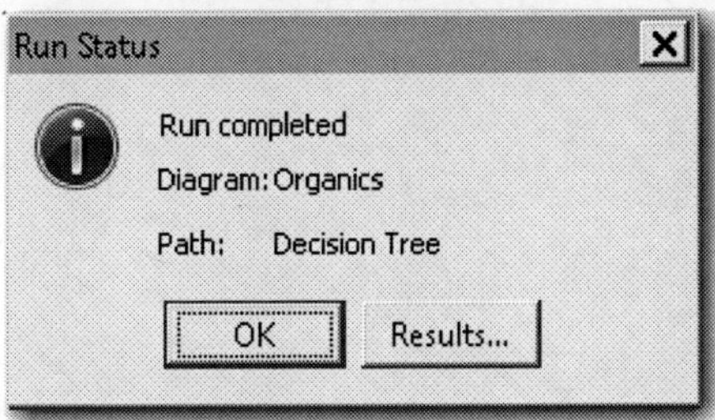


4) When the **Decision Tree** node run finishes, select Results... from the Run Status window. The Results window opens.

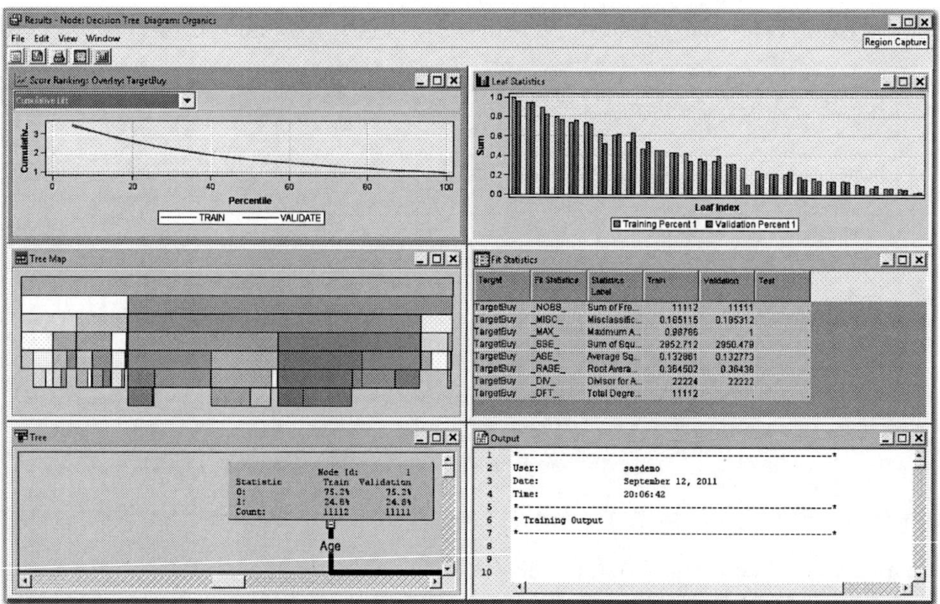

5) The easiest way to determine the number of leaves in your tree is via the Iteration plot. Select **View ⇨ Model ⇨ Subtree Assessment Plot** from the Result Window menu. The Iteration Plot window opens.

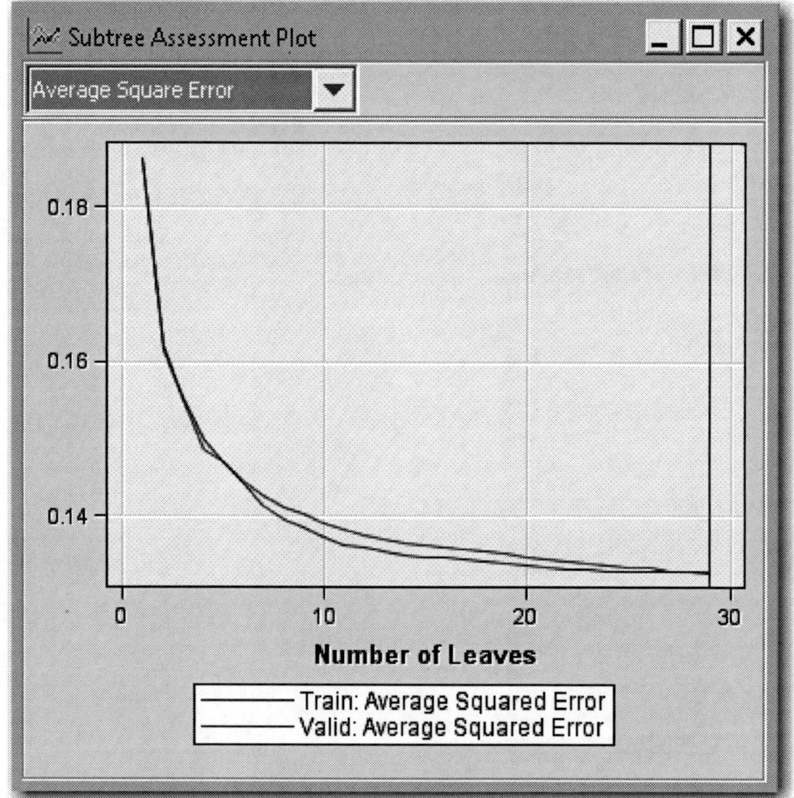


Using average squared error as the assessment measure results in a tree with 26 leaves.

**Which variable was used for the first split? What were the competing splits for this first split?**

These questions are best answered using interactive training.

6) Close the Results window for the Decision Tree model.

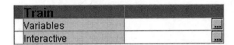

7) Select the Interactive ellipsis from the **Decision Tree** property panel. The SAS Enterprise Miner Tree Desktop Application window opens.

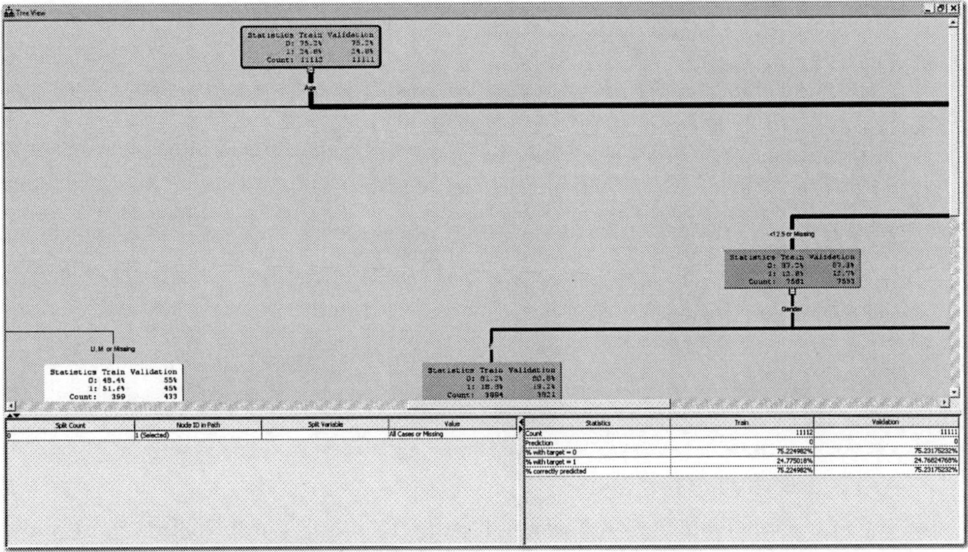

8) Maximize the Tree View window.

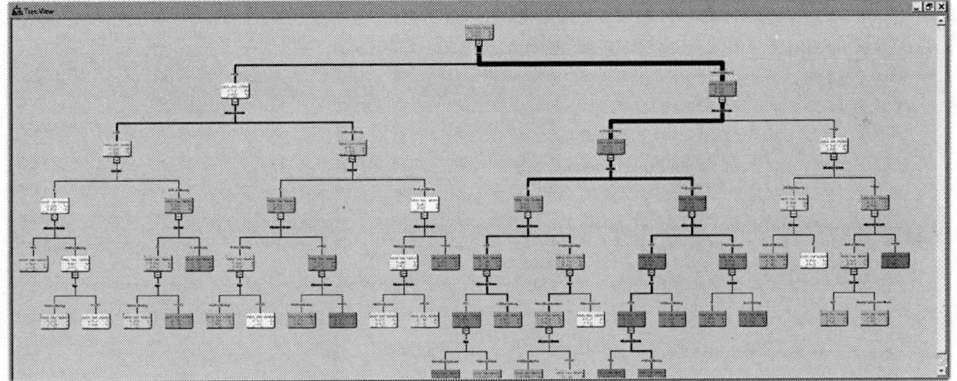

9) Right-click the root node and select **Split Node…** from the option menu. The Split Node 1 window opens with information answering the two questions.

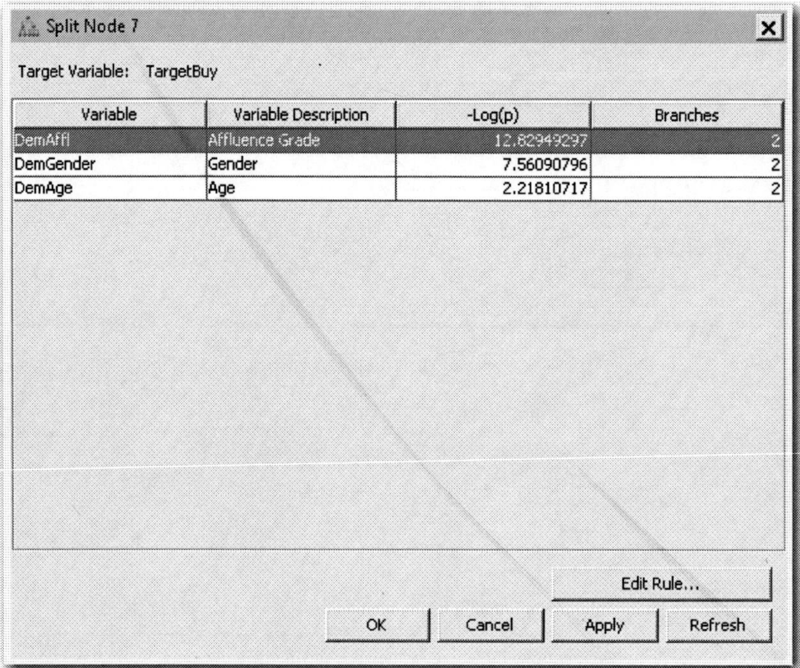
Split Node 7

Target Variable: TargetBuy

| Variable | Variable Description | -Log(p) | Branches |
|---|---|---|---|
| DemAffl | Affluence Grade | 12.82949297 | 2 |
| DemGender | Gender | 7.56090796 | 2 |
| DemAge | Age | 2.21810717 | 2 |

Edit Rule...

OK Cancel Apply Refresh

- Age is used for the first split.
- The competing splits are **Affluence Grade**, **Gender**, **Total Spend**, and **Loyalty Status**.

## 2. Predictive Modeling Using Regression

**a.** Return to the Organics diagram in the Exercises project. Connect the StatExplore tool to the **ORGANICS** data source as shown below in the diagram.

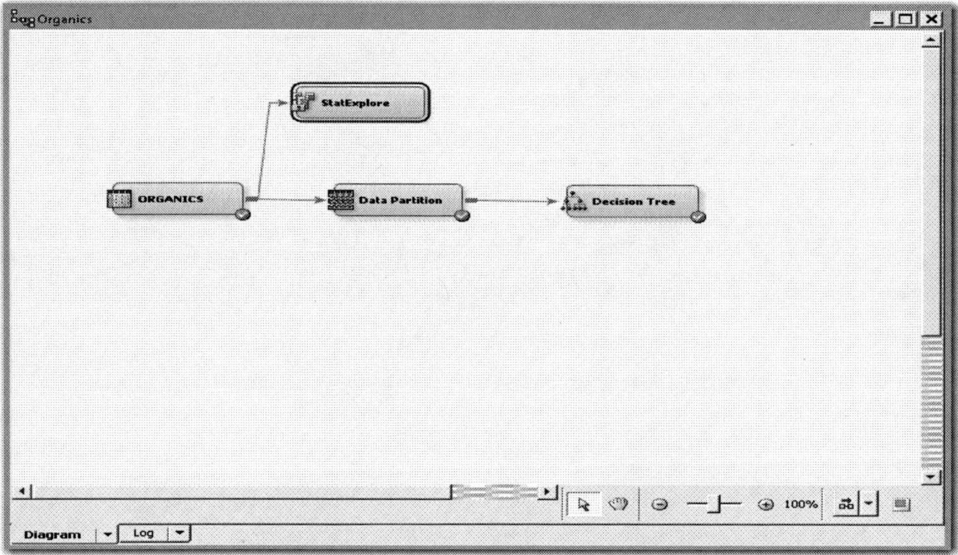

Run the StatExplore node and view the results.

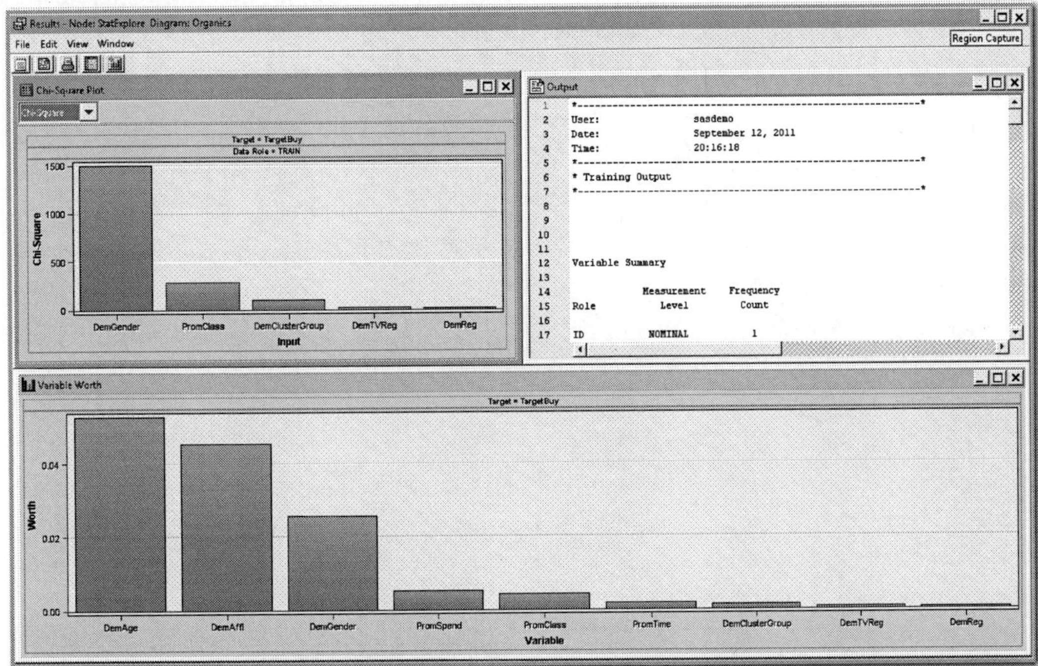


This exploration indicates those variables that have some worth in explaining the variability of the target variable.

**b.** In preparation for regression, is any missing values imputation needed? If yes, should you do this imputation before generating the decision tree models? Why or why not?

1) Go to line 40 in the Output window. Several of the class inputs have missing values.

Data Role=TRAIN

| Data Role | Variable Name | Role | Number of Levels | Missing | Mode | Mode Percentage | Mode | Mode2 Percentage |
|---|---|---|---|---|---|---|---|---|
| TRAIN | DemClusterGroup | INPUT | 8 | 674 | C | 20.55 | D | 19.70 |
| TRAIN | DemGender | INPUT | 4 | 2512 | F | 54.67 | M | 26.17 |
| TRAIN | DemReg | INPUT | 6 | 465 | South East | 38.85 | Midlands | 30.33 |
| TRAIN | DemTVReg | INPUT | 14 | 465 | London | 27.85 | Midlands | 14.05 |
| TRAIN | PromClass | INPUT | 4 | 0 | Silver | 38.57 | Tin | 29.19 |
| TRAIN | TargetBuy | TARGET | 2 | 0 | 0 | 75.23 | 1 | 24.77 |

2) Go to line 71 of the Output window. Most of the interval inputs also have missing values.

Data Role=TRAIN

| Variable | ROLE | Mean | Standard Deviation | Non Missing | Missing | Minimum | Median | Maximum | Skewness | Kurtosis |
|---|---|---|---|---|---|---|---|---|---|---|
| DemAffl | INPUT | 8.711893 | 3.421125 | 21138 | 1085 | 0 | 8 | 34 | 0.891684 | 2.09686 |
| DemAge | INPUT | 53.79715 | 13.20605 | 20715 | 1508 | 18 | 54 | 79 | -0.07983 | -0.84389 |
| PromSpend | INPUT | 4420.59 | 7559.048 | 22223 | 0 | 0.01 | 2000 | 296313.9 | 8.037186 | 184.8715 |
| PromTime | INPUT | 6.56467 | 4.657113 | 21942 | 281 | 0 | 5 | 39 | 2.28279 | 8.077622 |

You do not need to impute before the Decision Tree node. Decision trees have built-in ways to handle missing values.

c. Add an Impute node to the diagram and connect it to the **Data Partition** node. Set the node to impute "U" for unknown class variable values, the overall mean for unknown interval variable values, and create imputation indicators for all imputed inputs.

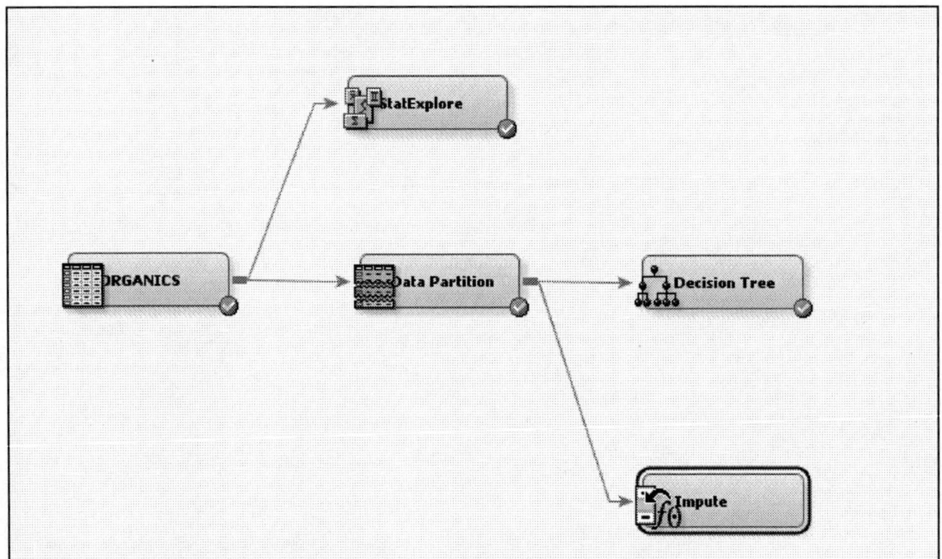


1) Select **Default Input Method** ⇨ **Default Constant Value**.

2) Type **U** for the Default Character Value property.

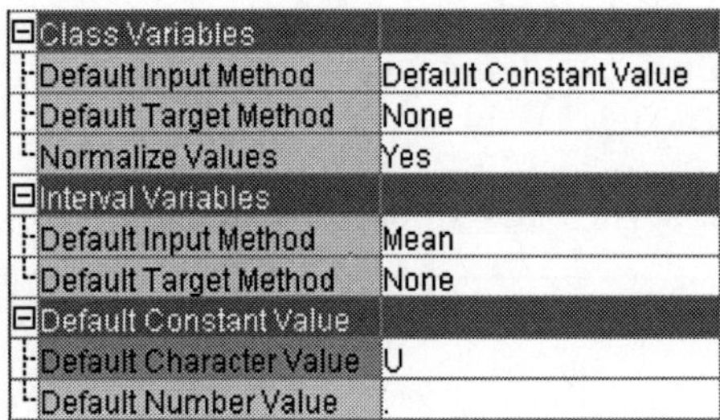

| Property | Value |
|---|---|
| ⊟ Class Variables | |
| Default Input Method | Default Constant Value |
| Default Target Method | None |
| Normalize Values | Yes |
| ⊟ Interval Variables | |
| Default Input Method | Mean |
| Default Target Method | None |
| ⊟ Default Constant Value | |
| Default Character Value | U |
| Default Number Value | . |

3) Select **Indicator Variable** ⇨ **Unique**.

4) Select **Indicator Variable Role** ⇨ **Input**.

| Score | |
|---|---|
| Hide Original Variables | Yes |
| Indicator Variable | Unique |
| Indicator Variable Role | Input |

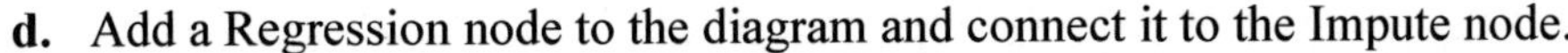

**d.** Add a Regression node to the diagram and connect it to the Impute node.

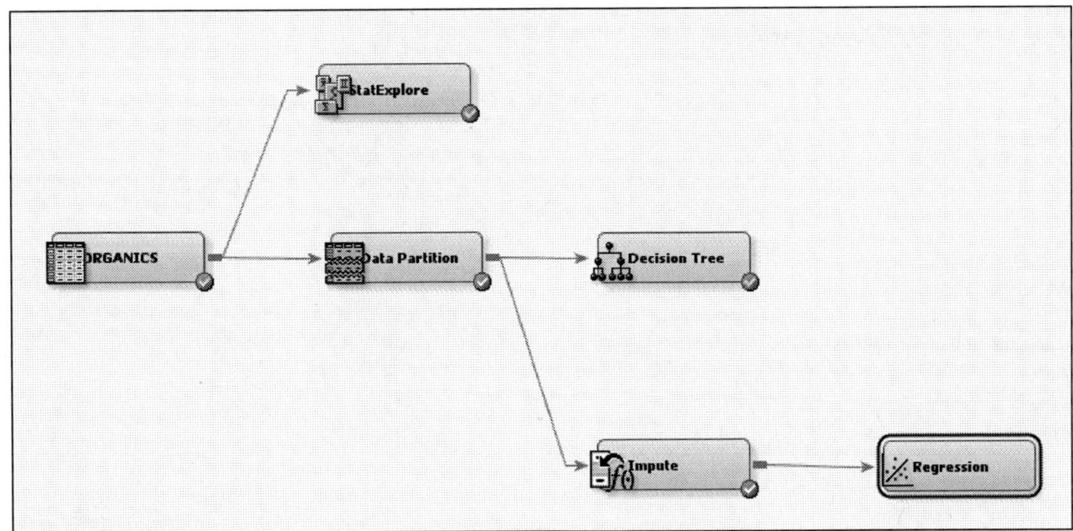


**e.** Choose the stepwise selection and average squared error as the selection criterion.

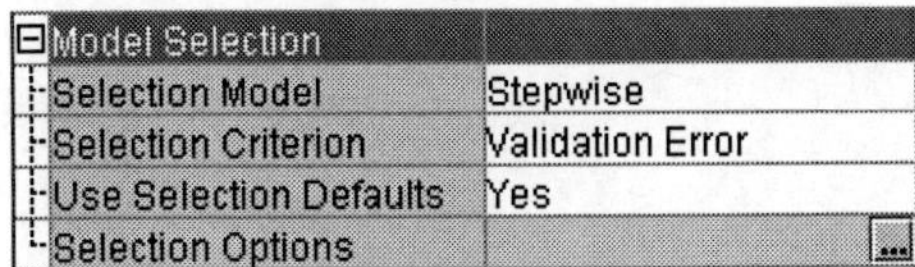

| Model Selection | |
|---|---|
| Selection Model | Stepwise |
| Selection Criterion | Validation Error |
| Use Selection Defaults | Yes |
| Selection Options | ... |

**f.** Run the Regression node and view the results. **Which variables are included in the final model? Which variables are important in this model? What is the validation ASE?**

The Results window opens.

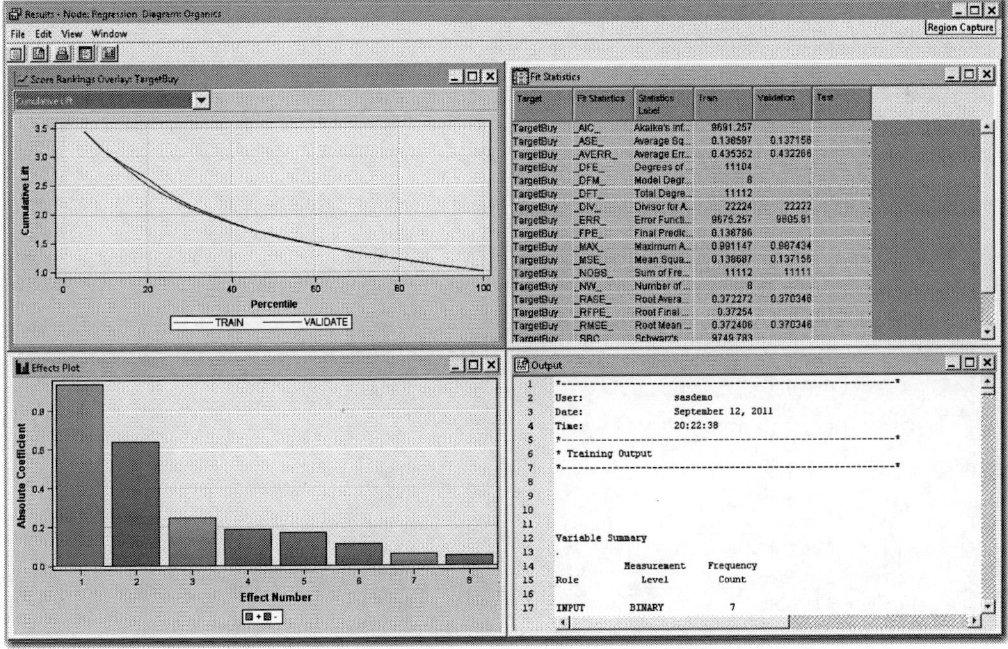

Go to line 664 in the Output window.

```
The selected model, based on the CHOOSE=VERROR criterion, is the model trained in Step 6. It
consists of the following effects:

Intercept  IMP_DemAffl  IMP_DemAge  IMP_DemGender  M_DemAffl  M_DemAge  M_DemGender
```

The odds ratios indicate the effect that each input has on the logit score.

```
                                                       Point
Effect                                              Estimate
IMP_DemAffl                                            1.283
IMP_DemAge                                             0.947
IMP_DemGender        F vs U                            6.967
IMP_DemGender        M vs U                            2.899
M_DemAffl            0 vs 1                            0.708
M_DemAge             0 vs 1                            0.796
M_DemGender          0 vs 1                            0.685
```

The validation ASE is given in the Fit Statistics window.

**Fit Statistics**

| Target | Fit Statistics | Statistics Label | Train | Validation | Test |
|---|---|---|---|---|---|
| TargetBuy | _AIC_ | Akaike's I... | 9691.257 | . | . |
| TargetBuy | _ASE_ | Average ... | 0.138587 | 0.137156 | . |
| TargetBuy | _AVERR_ | Average ... | 0.435352 | 0.432266 | . |
| TargetBuy | _DFE_ | Degrees ... | 11104 | . | . |
| TargetBuy | _DFM_ | Model De... | 8 | . | . |
| TargetBuy | _DFT_ | Total De... | 11112 | . | . |
| TargetBuy | _DIV_ | Divisor fo... | 22224 | 22222 | . |
| TargetBuy | _ERR_ | Error Fun... | 9675.257 | 9605.81 | . |
| TargetBuy | _FPE_ | Final Pre... | 0.138786 | . | . |
| TargetBuy | _MAX_ | Maximu... | 0.991147 | 0.987434 | . |
| TargetBuy | _MSE_ | Mean Sq... | 0.138687 | 0.137156 | . |
| TargetBuy | _NOBS_ | Sum of F... | 11112 | 11111 | . |
| TargetBuy | _NW_ | Number ... | 8 | . | . |
| TargetBuy | _RASE_ | Root Ave... | 0.372272 | 0.370346 | . |
| TargetBuy | _RFPE_ | Root Fin... | 0.37254 | . | . |
| TargetBuy | _RMSE_ | Root Mea... | 0.372406 | 0.370346 | . |
| TargetBuy | _SBC_ | Schwarz' | 9749.783 | | |

g. In preparation for regression, are any transformations of the data warranted? Why or why not?

1) Open the Variables window of the Partition node.

2) Select all interval inputs.

| Name | Partition Role | Role | Level |
|---|---|---|---|
| DemAffl | **Default** | Input | Interval |
| DemAge | **Default** | Input | Interval |
| DemCluster | **Default** | Rejected | Nominal |
| DemClusterGr | **Default** | Input | Nominal |
| DemGender | **Default** | Input | Nominal |
| DemReg | **Default** | Input | Nominal |
| DemTVReg | **Default** | Input | Nominal |
| ID | **Default** | ID | Nominal |
| PromClass | **Default** | Input | Nominal |
| PromSpend | **Default** | Input | Interval |
| PromTime | **Default** | Input | Interval |
| TargetAmt | **Default** | Rejected | Interval |
| TargetBuy | **Default** | Target | Binary |

3) Select Explore... . The Explore window opens.

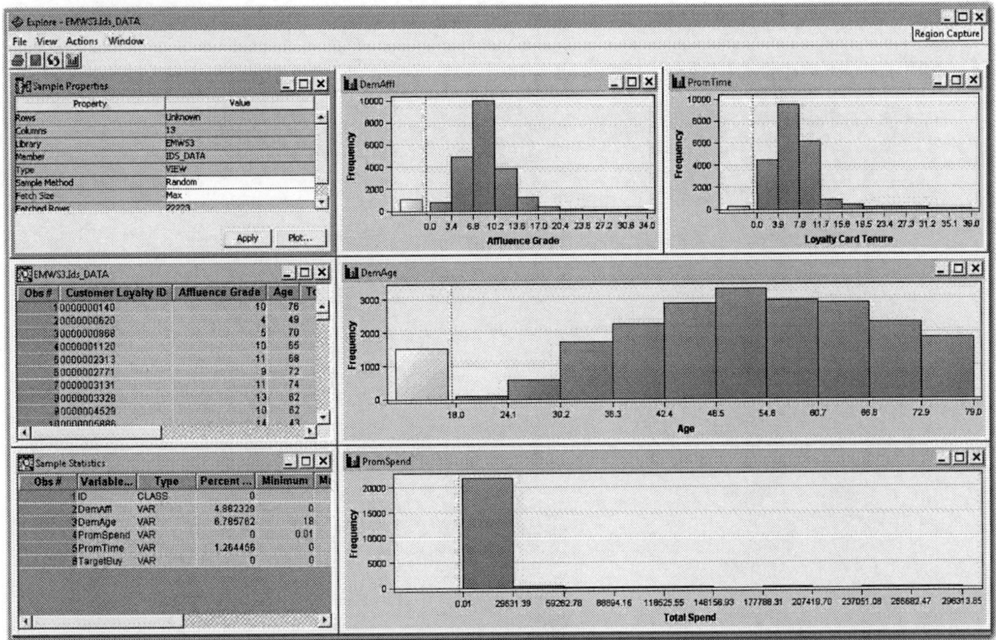

Both **Loyalty Card Tenure** and **Affluence Grade** have moderately skewed distributions, and **Total Spend** is really skewed. Applying a log transformation to these inputs might improve the model fit.

**h.** Disconnect the Impute node from the Data Partition node. Add a **Transform Variables** node to the diagram and connect it to the **Data Partition** node. Connect the Transform Variables node to the Impute node.

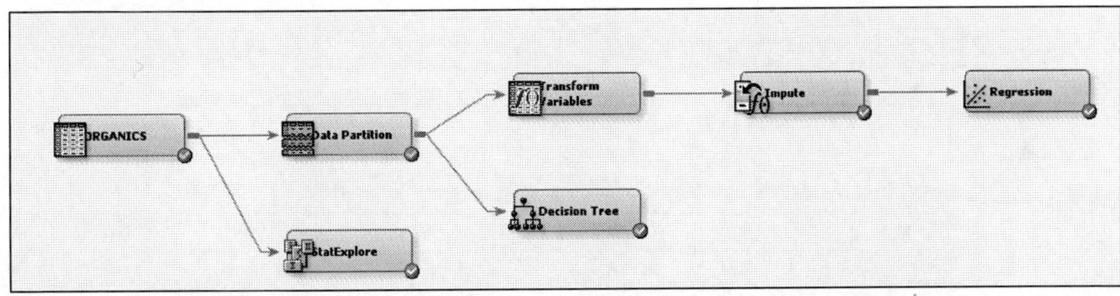

**i.** Apply a log transformation to the **DemAffl**, **PromSpend**, and **PromTime** inputs.

1) Open the Variables window of the Transform Variables node.

2) Select **Method** ⇨ **Log** for these inputs.

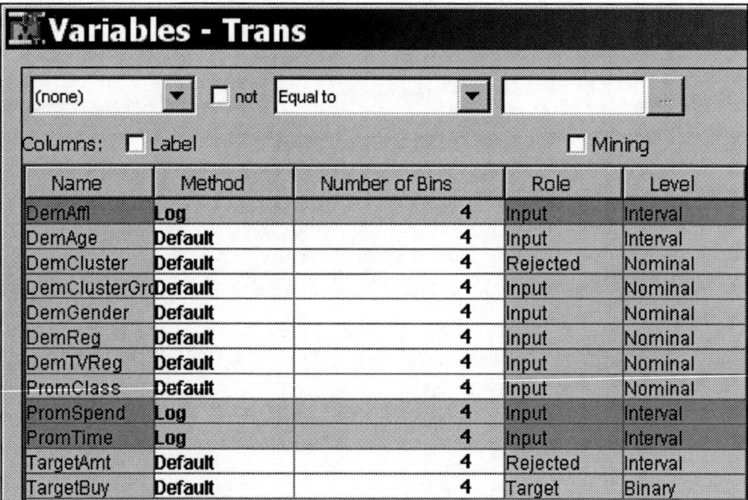


| Name | Method | Number of Bins | Role | Level |
|---|---|---|---|---|
| DemAffl | Log | 4 | Input | Interval |
| DemAge | Default | 4 | Input | Interval |
| DemCluster | Default | 4 | Rejected | Nominal |
| DemClusterGr | Default | 4 | Input | Nominal |
| DemGender | Default | 4 | Input | Nominal |
| DemReg | Default | 4 | Input | Nominal |
| DemTVReg | Default | 4 | Input | Nominal |
| PromClass | Default | 4 | Input | Nominal |
| PromSpend | Log | 4 | Input | Interval |
| PromTime | Log | 4 | Input | Interval |
| TargetAmt | Default | 4 | Rejected | Interval |
| TargetBuy | Default | 4 | Target | Binary |

3) Select OK to close the Variables window.

**j.** Run the **Transform Variables** node. Explore the exported training data. **Did the transformations result in less skewed distributions?**

1) The easiest way to explore the created inputs is to open the Variables window in the subsequent **Impute** node. Make sure that you update the Impute node before opening its Variables window.

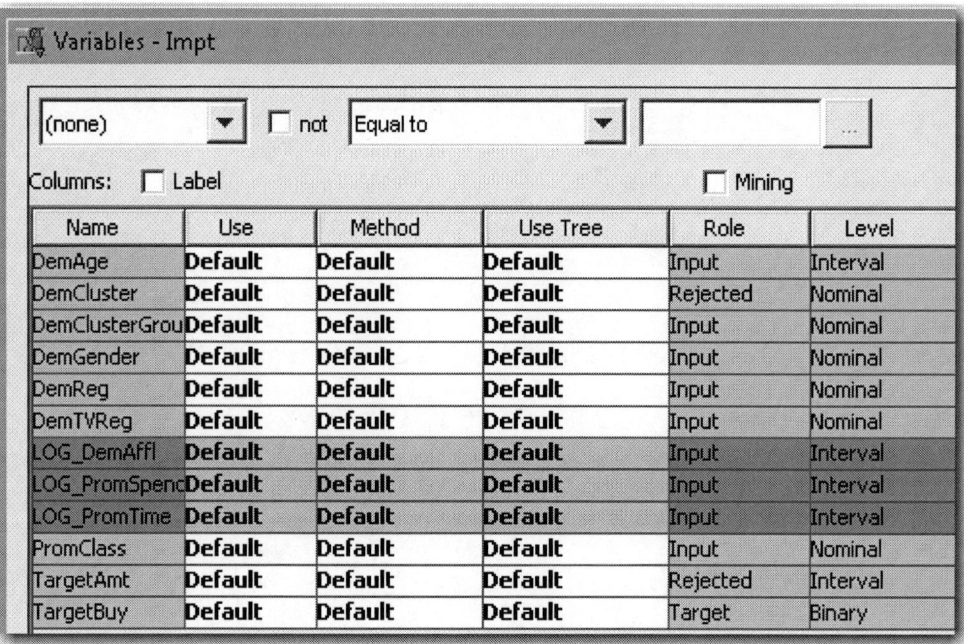


| Name | Use | Method | Use Tree | Role | Level |
|---|---|---|---|---|---|
| DemAge | Default | Default | Default | Input | Interval |
| DemCluster | Default | Default | Default | Rejected | Nominal |
| DemClusterGrou | Default | Default | Default | Input | Nominal |
| DemGender | Default | Default | Default | Input | Nominal |
| DemReg | Default | Default | Default | Input | Nominal |
| DemTVReg | Default | Default | Default | Input | Nominal |
| LOG_DemAffl | Default | Default | Default | Input | Interval |
| LOG_PromSpenc | Default | Default | Default | Input | Interval |
| LOG_PromTime | Default | Default | Default | Input | Interval |
| PromClass | Default | Default | Default | Input | Nominal |
| TargetAmt | Default | Default | Default | Rejected | Interval |
| TargetBuy | Default | Default | Default | Target | Binary |

2) With the **LOG_DemAffl**, **Log_PromSpend**, and **LOG_PromTime** inputs selected, select Explore... .

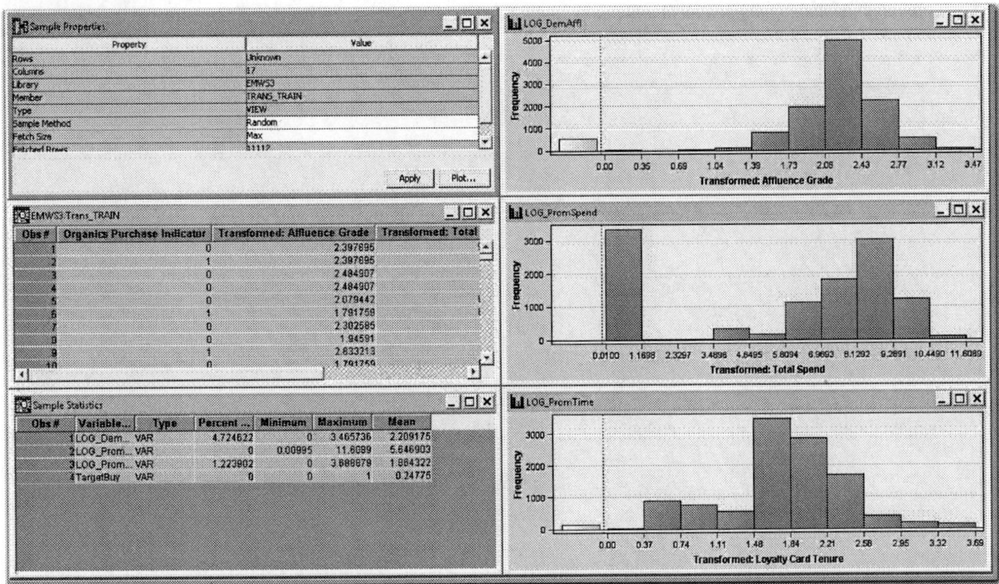

Two of the distributions are nicely symmetric, but the third is better except for the concentration of 0's. However, that transformed variable is probability a better predictor than the original variable.

**k.** Rerun the Regression node. **Do the selected variables change? How about the validation ASE?**

Go to line 664 of the Output window.

```
The selected model, based on the error rate for the validation data, is the model trained in Step 6. It consists of the following effects:

Intercept  IMP_DemAge  IMP_DemGender  IMP_LOG_DemAffl  M_DemAge  M_DemGender  M_LOG_DemAffl
```

The **IMP_LOG_DemAffl** and **M_LOG_DemAffl** replace **IMP_DemAffl** and **M_ _DemAffl**, respectively.

Apparently, the log transformation has actually increased validation ASE slightly.

**Fit Statistics**

| Target | Fit Statistics | Statistics Label | Train | Validation | Test |
|---|---|---|---|---|---|
| TargetBuy | _AIC_ | Akaike's I... | 9758.609 | . | . |
| TargetBuy | _ASE_ | Average ... | 0.139545 | 0.138204 | . |
| TargetBuy | _AVERR_ | Average ... | 0.438382 | 0.43599 | . |
| TargetBuy | _DFE_ | Degrees ... | 11104 | . | . |
| TargetBuy | _DFM_ | Model De... | 8 | . | . |
| TargetBuy | _DFT_ | Total De... | 11112 | . | . |
| TargetBuy | _DIV_ | Divisor fo... | 22224 | 22222 | . |
| TargetBuy | _ERR_ | Error Fun... | 9742.609 | 9688.581 | . |
| TargetBuy | _FPE_ | Final Pre... | 0.139746 | . | . |
| TargetBuy | _MAX_ | Maximu... | 0.992317 | 0.994405 | . |
| TargetBuy | _MSE_ | Mean Sq... | 0.139646 | 0.138204 | . |
| TargetBuy | _NOBS_ | Sum of F... | 11112 | 11111 | . |
| TargetBuy | _NW_ | Number ... | 8 | . | . |
| TargetBuy | _RASE_ | Root Ave... | 0.373557 | 0.371759 | . |
| TargetBuy | _RFPE_ | Root Fin... | 0.373826 | . | . |
| TargetBuy | _RMSE_ | Root Mea... | 0.373692 | 0.371759 | . |

l. Create a full second-degree polynomial model. **How does the validation average squared error for the polynomial model compare to the original model?**

1) Copy and paste the **Regression** node to the diagram and rename it Polynomial Regression.

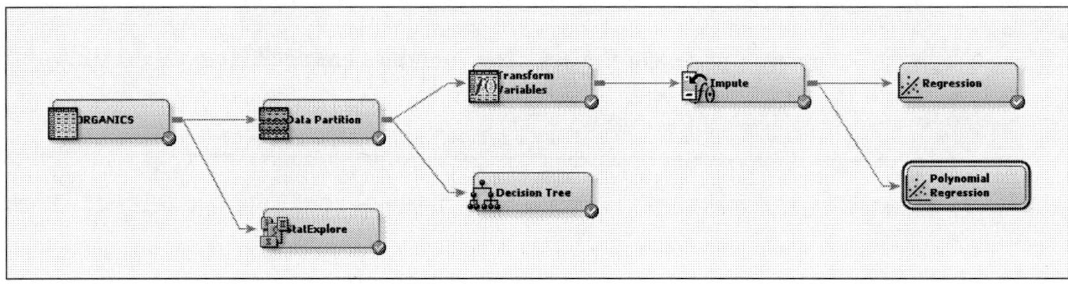

2) Make the indicated changes to the Polynomial Regression Properties panel.

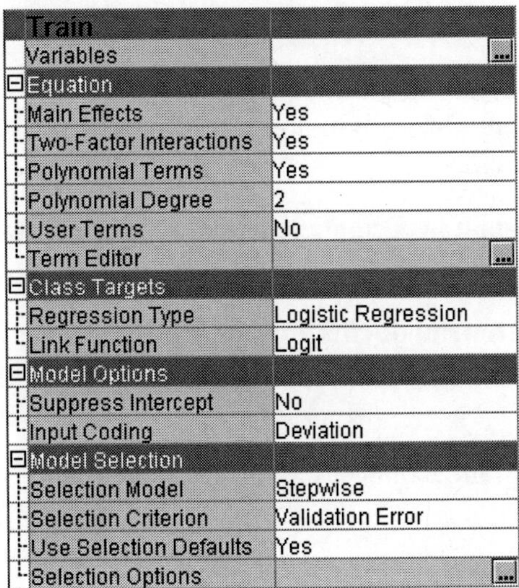

| Train | |
|---|---|
| Variables | ... |
| **Equation** | |
| Main Effects | Yes |
| Two-Factor Interactions | Yes |
| Polynomial Terms | Yes |
| Polynomial Degree | 2 |
| User Terms | No |
| Term Editor | ... |
| **Class Targets** | |
| Regression Type | Logistic Regression |
| Link Function | Logit |
| **Model Options** | |
| Suppress Intercept | No |
| Input Coding | Deviation |
| **Model Selection** | |
| Selection Model | Stepwise |
| Selection Criterion | Validation Error |
| Use Selection Defaults | Yes |
| Selection Options | ... |

3) Go to line 1598

```
The selected model, based on the CHOOSE=VERROR criterion, is the model trained in Step 7. It
consists of the following effects:

Intercept  IMP_DemAge  IMP_DemGender  IMP_LOG_DemAffl  M_DemAge  M_DemGender*M_LOG_DemAffl
IMP_DemAge*IMP_DemAge  IMP_LOG_DemAffl*IMP_LOG_DemAffl
```

The Polynomial Regression node adds a few additional interaction terms.

4) Examine the Fit Statistics window.

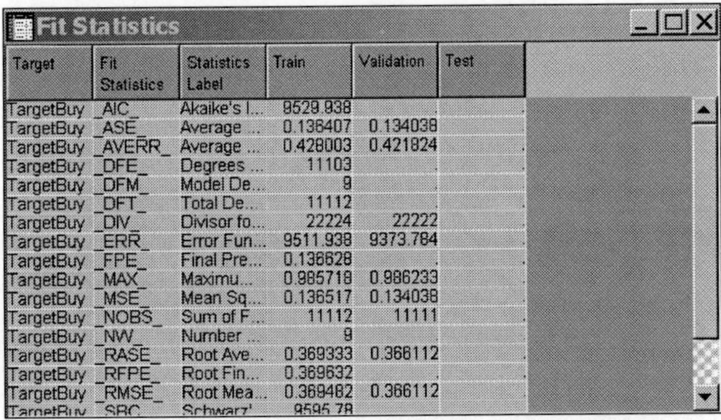

Fit Statistics

| Target | Fit Statistics | Statistics Label | Train | Validation | Test |
|---|---|---|---|---|---|
| TargetBuy | _AIC_ | Akaike's I... | 8529.938 | . | . |
| TargetBuy | _ASE_ | Average ... | 0.136407 | 0.134038 | . |
| TargetBuy | _AVERR_ | Average ... | 0.428003 | 0.421824 | . |
| TargetBuy | _DFE_ | Degrees ... | 11103 | . | . |
| TargetBuy | _DFM_ | Model De... | 9 | . | . |
| TargetBuy | _DFT_ | Total De... | 11112 | . | . |
| TargetBuy | _DIV_ | Divisor fo... | 22224 | 22222 | . |
| TargetBuy | _ERR_ | Error Fun... | 9511.938 | 9373.784 | . |
| TargetBuy | _FPE_ | Final Pre... | 0.136628 | . | . |
| TargetBuy | _MAX_ | Maximu... | 0.985718 | 0.986233 | . |
| TargetBuy | _MSE_ | Mean Sq... | 0.136517 | 0.134038 | . |
| TargetBuy | _NOBS_ | Sum of F... | 11112 | 11111 | . |
| TargetBuy | _NW_ | Number ... | 9 | . | . |
| TargetBuy | _RASE_ | Root Ave... | 0.369333 | 0.366112 | . |
| TargetBuy | _RFPE_ | Root Fin... | 0.369632 | . | . |
| TargetBuy | _RMSE_ | Root Mea... | 0.369482 | 0.366112 | . |
| TargetBuy | _SBC_ | Schwarz' | 9595.78 | | |

The additional terms reduce validation ASE, slightly.

**3. Predictive Modeling Using Neural Networks**

**a.** In preparation for a neural network model, is imputation of missing values needed? Why or why not?

**Yes. Neural network models, as well as most models relying on a prediction formula, require a complete record for both modeling and scoring.**

**b.** In preparation for a neural network model, is data transformation generally needed? Why or why not?

**Not necessarily. Neural network models create transformations of inputs for use in a regression-like model. However, having input distributions with low skewness and kurtosis tends to result in more stable models.**

**c.** Add a Neural Network tool to the Organics diagram. Connect the Impute node to the Neural Network node.

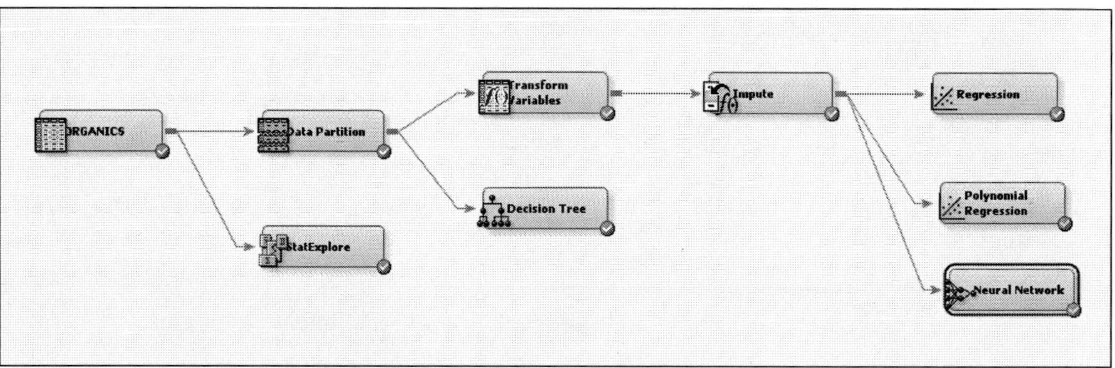


**d.** Set the model selection criterion to average error.

| Property | Value |
|---|---|
| General | |
| Node ID | Neural |
| Imported Data | ... |
| Exported Data | ... |
| Notes | ... |
| Train | |
| Variables | ... |
| Network | ... |
| Model Selection Criterior | Average Error |
| Use Current Estimates | No |
| Train Options | |
| Maximum Iterations | 20 |
| Maximum Time | 4 Hours |
| Training Technique | Default |
| Preliminary Training Opt | |
| Preliminary Training | Yes |
| Maximum Iterations | 10 |
| Maximum Time | 1 Hour |
| Number of Runs | 5 |
| Convergence Criteria | |
| Uses Defaults | Yes |
| Options | ... |
| Print Options | |
| Suppress Output | No |

**e.** Run the **Neural Network** node and examine the validation average squared error. How does it compare to other models?

The Result window should appear as shown below.

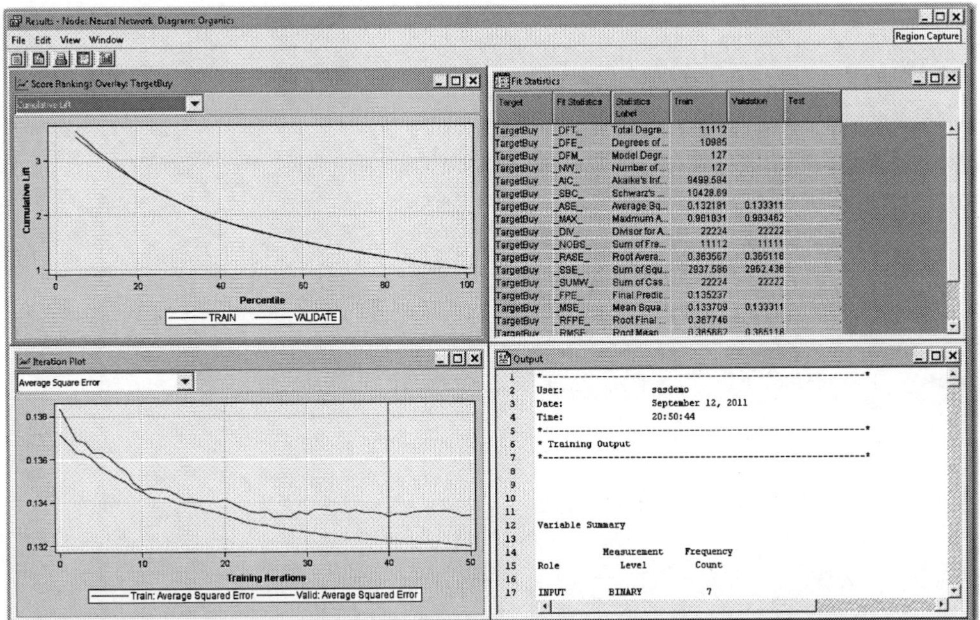

Examine the Fit Statistics window.

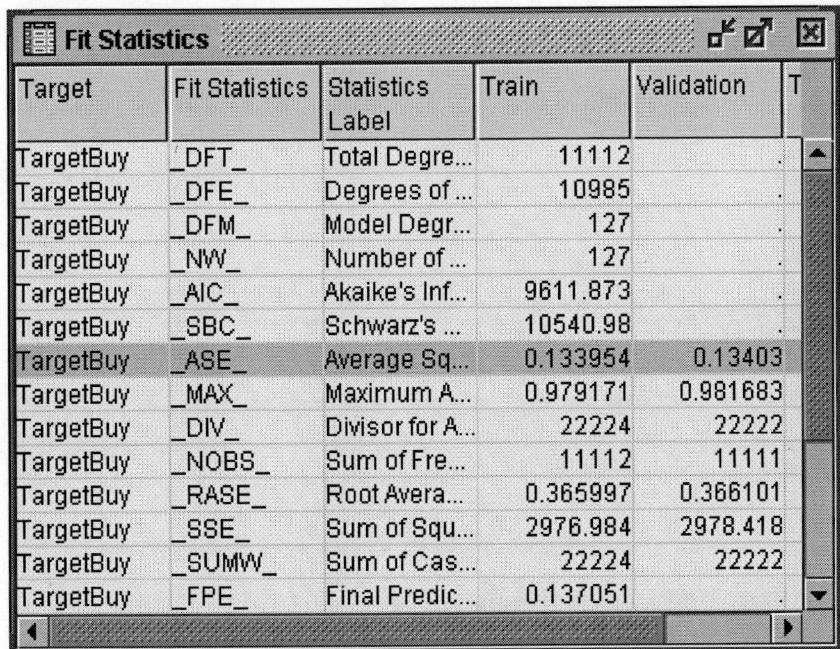

Fit Statistics

| Target | Fit Statistics | Statistics Label | Train | Validation | T |
|---|---|---|---|---|---|
| TargetBuy | _DFT_ | Total Degre... | 11112 | | . |
| TargetBuy | _DFE_ | Degrees of ... | 10985 | | . |
| TargetBuy | _DFM_ | Model Degr... | 127 | | . |
| TargetBuy | _NW_ | Number of ... | 127 | | . |
| TargetBuy | _AIC_ | Akaike's Inf... | 9611.873 | | . |
| TargetBuy | _SBC_ | Schwarz's ... | 10540.98 | | . |
| TargetBuy | _ASE_ | Average Sq... | 0.133954 | 0.13403 | |
| TargetBuy | _MAX_ | Maximum A... | 0.979171 | 0.981683 | |
| TargetBuy | _DIV_ | Divisor for A... | 22224 | 22222 | |
| TargetBuy | _NOBS_ | Sum of Fre... | 11112 | 11111 | |
| TargetBuy | _RASE_ | Root Avera... | 0.365997 | 0.366101 | |
| TargetBuy | _SSE_ | Sum of Squ... | 2976.984 | 2978.418 | |
| TargetBuy | _SUMW_ | Sum of Cas... | 22224 | 22222 | |
| TargetBuy | _FPE_ | Final Predic... | 0.137051 | | . |

The validation ASE for the neural network model is slightly smaller than the standard regression, about the same as the polynomial regression, and slightly larger than the decision tree.

**4. Scoring Organics Data**

**a.** Create a Score data source for the **ScoreOrganics** data.

1) Select **File** ⇨ **New** ⇨ **Data Source**.

2) Proceed to step 2 of the Data Source Wizard by selecting Next >.

3) Select the **GARPM.ScoreOrganics** data set.

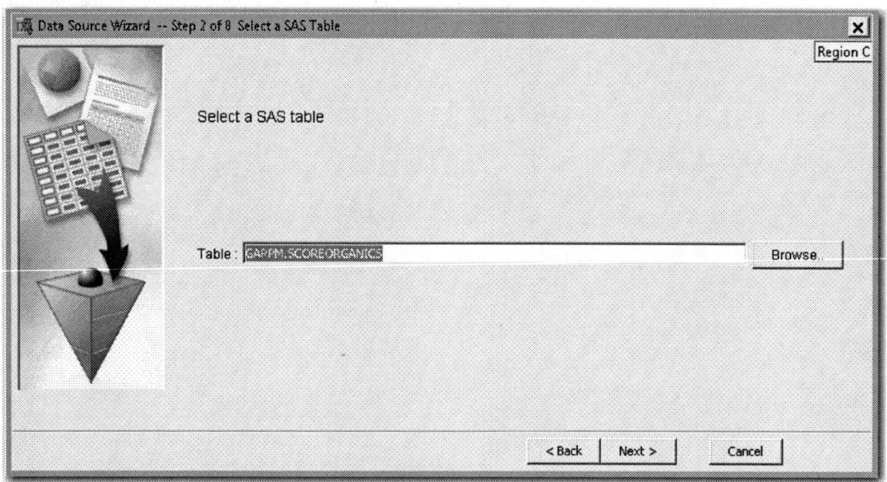


4) Proceed to step 6 of the Data Source Wizard.

5) Select **Role** ⇨ **Score**.

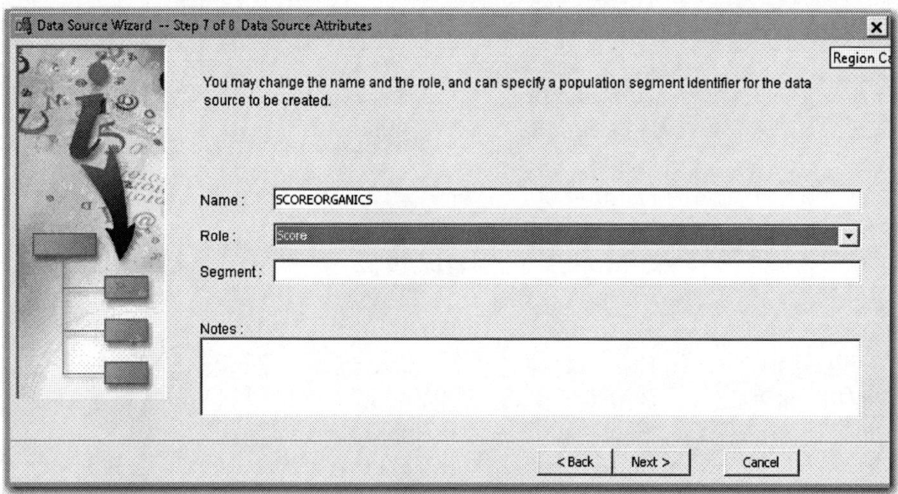


6) Select Next > and then select Finish.

**b.** Score the **ScoreOrganics** data using the model selected with the Model Comparison node.

1) Connect a Score tool to the Model Comparison node.

2) Connect a ScoreOrganics data source to the Score node.

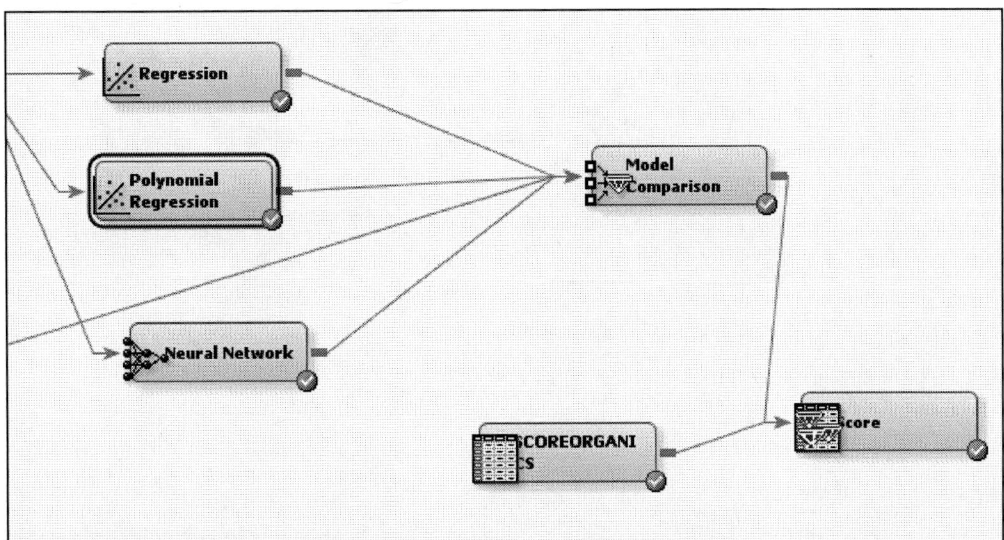


3) Run the Score node.

4) Browse the Exported data from the Score node to confirm the scoring process.

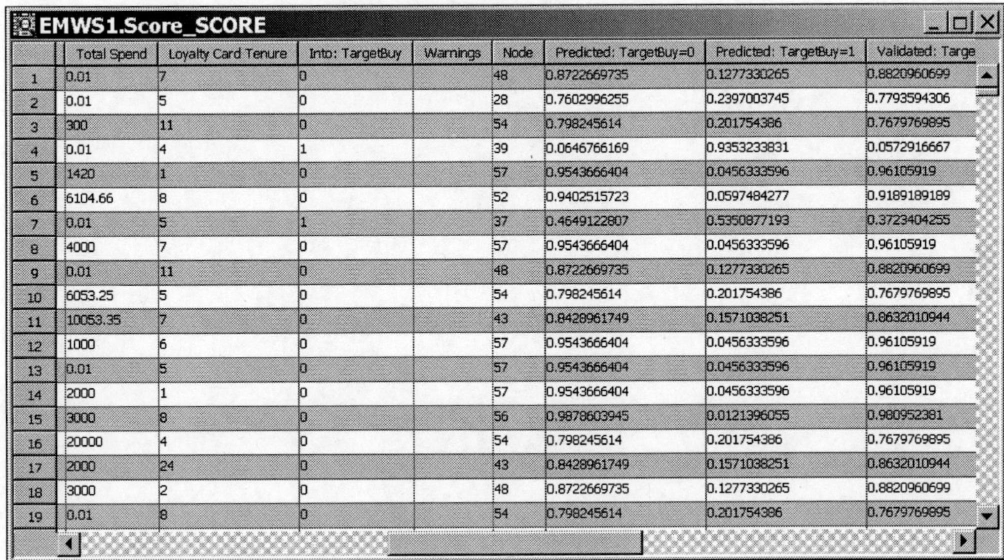

EMWS1.Score_SCORE

| | Total Spend | Loyalty Card Tenure | Into: TargetBuy | Warnings | Node | Predicted: TargetBuy=0 | Predicted: TargetBuy=1 | Validated: Targe |
|---|---|---|---|---|---|---|---|---|
| 1 | 0.01 | 7 | 0 | | 48 | 0.8722669735 | 0.1277330265 | 0.8820960699 |
| 2 | 0.01 | 5 | 0 | | 28 | 0.7602996255 | 0.2397003745 | 0.7793594306 |
| 3 | 300 | 11 | 0 | | 54 | 0.798245614 | 0.201754386 | 0.7679769895 |
| 4 | 0.01 | 4 | 1 | | 39 | 0.0646766169 | 0.9353233831 | 0.0572916667 |
| 5 | 1420 | 1 | 0 | | 57 | 0.9543666404 | 0.0456333596 | 0.96105919 |
| 6 | 6104.66 | 8 | 0 | | 52 | 0.9402515723 | 0.0597484277 | 0.9189189189 |
| 7 | 0.01 | 5 | 1 | | 37 | 0.4649122807 | 0.5350877193 | 0.3723404255 |
| 8 | 4000 | 7 | 0 | | 57 | 0.9543666404 | 0.0456333596 | 0.96105919 |
| 9 | 0.01 | 11 | 0 | | 48 | 0.8722669735 | 0.1277330265 | 0.8820960699 |
| 10 | 6053.25 | 5 | 0 | | 54 | 0.798245614 | 0.201754386 | 0.7679769895 |
| 11 | 10053.35 | 7 | 0 | | 43 | 0.8428961749 | 0.1571038251 | 0.8632010944 |
| 12 | 1000 | 6 | 0 | | 57 | 0.9543666404 | 0.0456333596 | 0.96105919 |
| 13 | 0.01 | 5 | 0 | | 57 | 0.9543666404 | 0.0456333596 | 0.96105919 |
| 14 | 2000 | 1 | 0 | | 57 | 0.9543666404 | 0.0456333596 | 0.96105919 |
| 15 | 3000 | 8 | 0 | | 56 | 0.9878603945 | 0.0121396055 | 0.980952381 |
| 16 | 20000 | 4 | 0 | | 54 | 0.798245614 | 0.201754386 | 0.7679769895 |
| 17 | 2000 | 24 | 0 | | 43 | 0.8428961749 | 0.1571038251 | 0.8632010944 |
| 18 | 3000 | 2 | 0 | | 48 | 0.8722669735 | 0.1277330265 | 0.8820960699 |
| 19 | 0.01 | 8 | 0 | | 54 | 0.798245614 | 0.201754386 | 0.7679769895 |

A successfully scored data set will feature predicted probabilities and prediction decisions in the last three columns.